The Stress of Battle
Quantifying Human
Performance in Combat

Front cover illustration

A Chieftain tank of the Queen's Own Hussars, part of the defence forces on Exercise White Ermine. The vehicle is fitted with SIMFIRE and DOAE monitoring equipment (including video recorder capturing both gunner's view and crew intercom).

Back cover illustration

Example of result from Historical Analysis of World War II anti-armour combat (largely from anti-tank guns illustrated at inset). The results show the importance of individual heroic behaviour to tank killing effectiveness (the 'T' factor described inside).

The Stress of Battle
Quantifying Human Performance in Combat
David Rowland

London: TSO

Published by TSO (The Stationery Office) and available from:

Online
www.tsoshop.co.uk

Mail, Telephone, Fax & E-mail
TSO
PO Box 29, Norwich, NR3 1GN
Telephone orders/General enquiries: 0870 600 5522
Fax orders: 0870 600 5533
E-mail: book.orders@tso.co.uk
Textphone 0870 240 3701

TSO Shops
123 Kingsway, London, WC2B 6PQ
020 7242 6393 Fax 020 7242 6394
68-69 Bull Street, Birmingham B4 6AD
0121 236 9696 Fax 0121 236 9699
9-21 Princess Street, Manchester M60 8AS
0161 834 7201 Fax 0161 833 0634
16 Arthur Street, Belfast BT1 4GD
028 9023 8451 Fax 028 9023 5401
18-19 High Street, Cardiff CF10 1PT
029 2039 5548 Fax 029 2038 4347
71 Lothian Road, Edinburgh EH3 9AZ
0870 606 5566 Fax 0870 606 5588

TSO Accredited Agents
(see Yellow Pages)

and through good booksellers

ISBN 0 11 773046 7

Contents

Foreword

My first contact with operational analysis (OA) was in the
mid-1950s, when my father, a Regular officer, served a stint at
the Army Operational Research Group (AORG) at Broadoaks
in Surrey. A little more than a decade later I, too, was a serving
officer and was attached to the Headquarters 7th Armoured
Brigade during Exercise Helltank, the field trial conducted
by AORG's successor, the Defence Operational Analysis
Establishment (DOAE), as part of its study on the effectiveness
of anti-tank helicopters. It was then that I first met the members
of the Field Studies Division of DOAE who were in the company
of an officer in my regiment who was already making a name
for himself as a military historian, Major Kenneth Macksey.

Helltank gave me an insight into some of the work that DOAE
was doing, but it was not to be for a further fifteen years or so
that I was to become actively involved with OA. By then I had
forsaken the sword for the pen and was pursuing a second career
as a military historian. I was put in contact with David Rowland,
who was about to begin an investigation into breakthroughs
and needed an historian to assist him in gathering together data
on breakthrough operations throughout the 20th century. It was
the beginning of an association with both David and the field
of historical analysis which lasts to this day.

While the armed forces have always acknowledged the value of
military history, their approach to it has traditionally been rather
narrow. Indeed, the emphasis was largely on the study of the great
commanders, in the hope that succeeding generations of soldiers,
sailors, and airmen might emulate them, and on the deeds of
previous generations so that they might inspire those following
on behind. Very recent experience has been used as the basis for
developing operational doctrine, but the tendency has been to
dismiss anything that went before as not relevant on the basis of
technological changes in warfare. Thus, the mass of data which has

been preserved in the form of war diaries, ships' logs, operational record books, after action reports, and the like were the preserve merely of historians and were largely ignored by the armed forces.

This book sets out to dispel the myth that history has little relevance to military operations in the 21st century. David Rowland shows how the introduction of laser simulation training aids into the British Army in the 1970s not only resulted in more realistic data being incorporated in models for developing new weapons and equipment and optimising the use of those in service, but that they also revealed the degree of degradation in weapons performance compared with that achieved on the firing range. It was this that triggered the question of how much more degradation would there be on the actual battlefield. On the surface, quantification of this appeared impossible. True, some work had been done on the World War 2 and Korean experience, but the evidence was mainly anecdotal and the conclusions largely subjective. The British Army's later experience during the 1950s, 1960s, and 1970s had mainly been in the realm of counter-insurgency and there was little meaningful data available for modern conventional warfare.

It was the realisation that the effectiveness of small arms and machine guns had not changed dramatically over the past 150 years that led David Rowland to adopt a new approach – historical analysis. Combining this with more traditional analytical tools enabled him to establish degradation factors for infantry combat. Tackling the armour/anti-armour battle was more problematical, because here technology had significantly improved weapons effectiveness. Even so, using a more indirect approach enabled this problem to be overcome as well. It also revealed the influence of heroic behaviour. David Rowland and his colleagues then went on to investigate the effect of shock and surprise on combat degradation, again drawing much on historical analysis.

Rowland's account of how historical analysis came to play such a significant part in OA makes fascinating reading. Not only does he reveal fresh insights into what actually happens on the battlefield, but he also shows how multi-disciplined OA now is, drawing as it does on many branches of science, including psychology. He has also convincingly demonstrated that military history has a new more practical use in helping to answer questions on contemporary and future military operations. The result is a book which will be of much interest to not just those involved in operational analysis, but also to anyone connected with defence matters and to military historians.

Over the past twenty years the value and significance of historical analysis has become increasingly recognised and it is now widely accepted as a legitimate branch of OA. I, for one, feel very privileged to have been closely associated with a number of HA projects. In particular, it has been both a pleasure and a very stimulating experience to have worked with David Rowland, the acknowledged father of HA, on many of them.

London   CHARLES MESSENGER
October 2005

THE STRESS OF BATTLE

Introduction

Substantial investments in military weapons and equipment are made by most countries. Military success and the avoidance of unnecessary casualties are dependant on their effective use in combat; this in turn is governed by the limitations of individuals' behaviour in the face of the dangers of live fire. However, the effects of these dangers on combat behaviour have received relatively little measurement or analysis. Indeed, because of the dangers of battle, the longer term goals of monitoring performance have naturally been subjugated to the immediate goals of winning, or even of just surviving, in battle.

The Field Studies Division of the Defence Operational Analysis Establishment (DOAE) had an overall tasking to conduct research into factors affecting combat. This was intended to be by field trials, which could include, for example, detection trials, terrain surveys or observation of military Field Training Exercises. However, all of these suffered drawbacks due to the relatively calm and non-competitive situations from which data was collected, even before the absence of danger is considered.

When the Army began experimenting with the use of weapon simulation for training in the early 1970s we were able to propose the study of more realistic combat interactions. We proposed to do this through measurement and observation of the interactive exercises which could be set up using these systems. We were able to plan and, with considerable military help, conduct a novel series of exercises from which it was possible to collect extra data on this quasi-combat for analysis and reconstruction of the battles fought.

At the time we could not envisage that these exercises with their lorry loads of collected data would be able to give us the unique basis which would lead us on to real combat performance too, but they did, also providing the essential route in.

Viewed in retrospect, these trials were only possible in a limited window in time: any earlier and they would not have been technically feasible. The sequence of trials (of armoured combat, close combat and reconnaissance) lasted from 1975 until 1988. Then, shortly thereafter, force reductions and increasing restrictions on the use of training exercises across the German countryside, rendered field training exercises increasingly difficult.

Within this window we designed, and analysed results from, many simulated battles of up to battalion and squadron/company level in UK and FRG. The hundreds of simulated battles which we observed and analysed, fulfilled their intended purpose of examining the physical limits of tactical combat in a range of terrains. They also provided us with measurements which not only prompted comparisons with real combat but aided that process.

For real combat the relatively little data and few measurements available tend to be much more scattered or dispersed than those from our trials results. However, as is shown in this book, the detailed exercise data and its variability due to chance factors (such as detection probability and probability of hit when engaging) have enabled us to work progressively through sets of combat data, breaking into this hitherto largely intractable problem.

Once inside this area, and with increasing knowledge of the structures, we found that we were able to tackle successive problems and hence to provide improving quantitative relationships. This narrative is intended to outline this detective story and to present some of its emerging conclusions. These have surprised many by the scales of effect revealed.

This account covers the relevant parts of my work for MoD through DOAE and its successors for the last 30 years, initially as a civil service scientist , then more recently, after retirement, as a contractor to the Historical Analysis section (through HVR Limited and presently through Newman and Spurr Consultancy Ltd).

To have been so closely involved throughout this process, which has provided a sequence of fascinating insights has been a privilege, as well as a challenge. Many others have contributed to parts of the process, so many that I have to acknowledge them as members of groups rather than by name. Given the genesis of this work I must first mention all those involved in the series of exercises on which our trials were based; these include:

- Members of the DOAE Trials Group who set up, instrumented and ran the technical aspects of the Exercises.

- The Military officers seconded to the Field Studies Division who entered wholeheartedly into the planning and military control of the Exercises to achieve our study aims, whilst providing unique training to the troops.

- The members of all those military units and sub-units who took part in the trials series (CHINESE EYE, DRAGONS EYE I & II, KINGS RIDE I to V & WHITE ERMINE I to III) for their wholehearted participation, as well as all of those who helped to run these smoothly including Service Liaison Officers, Damage Control, Claims Officers and Military and Civil Police.

- The analysts in Field Studies Division who conducted the extensive data reduction and analysis on which some of the overall analyses here are based.

- In developing from the exercise analysis:

- The analysts, both civil and military, who formed the fledgling Historical Analysis section, allowing us to fit a growing programme into the continuing field trial commitments.

- The historians who have adapted their disciplines to provide us with the basic historical data needed for the succession of studies, whether they helped with one or many studies. These include the Service Historical Branches and those individuals who worked with us on contract.

- The successive members of the Historical Analysis Section who as analysts, managers or support staff have made contributions enabling HA studies to grow and develop to meet a variety of needs.

- The management of DOAE and its successor organisations: DOAC,CDA,DERA and Dstl who have encouraged the evolution and development of the work described to answer MOD's needs.

- The MOD sponsors, both military and civil who have posed successive questions and provided resources to further thcsc studies for both their long and short term needs.

In addition to sponsors, the constructive interest in the emerging results, which has been shown by military officers and analysts, has also been both an encouragement and acted to prompt the review and questioning results, leading to more robust findings.

My thanks must also go to my family for their support and encouragement with the various phases of this work including the lengthy paper invasion of our dining table for prototype analyses and historical reconstructions.

Specific thanks for helping in the preparation of this volume are owed to Charles Messenger for his major editorial input, particularly appropriate in view of his long standing association with HA as a contributing historian.

My thanks also go to those who have co-ordinated and managed its preparation and to Sandra Hudson, Jan Hutchings and Val Keirl for painstakingly interpreting my manuscript drafts and for transforming these into a clear layout.

However any faults, errors or omissions are the responsibility of the author.

CHAPTER ONE
Introduction to Operational Research and Historical Analysis

Throughout the ages, the impact of science on war has become increasingly marked. Much of it has concerned technical innovation and intelligence. Another field of military science, which has gained increasing prominence during the last 100 years has been the study of operational problems with the aim of providing advice to military commanders and others. Operational Analysis (OA) or Operational Research (OR), as it is termed, draws on a wide range of scientific disciplines and is equally applicable to the civilian world.

The official history of Operational Research in the RAF,[1] published some 40 years ago, defines OR as 'numerical thinking about operations, with the aim of formulating conclusions which, applied to operations, may give a profitable return for a given level of effort'. It applies not just to military operations *per se*, but also to equipment design, doctrine, and training. Yet, the origins of OR lie far back in time even if they did not all involve numerical analysis. One official publication claims:

> 'The origins of Operational Analysis can be traced back two thousand years to the campaigns of Alexander the Great, for he was in the habit of talking with his group of philosophers who would gather around the camp fire when the day's battle was done, discuss the lessons learned and propose courses of action for the morrow.'[2]

The precepts set out by Sun Tzu in China around 500 BC in his *The Art of War* have also been suggested as OR but appear to be more the percipience of an experienced soldier. This phenomenon has recurred throughout history, with some commanders developing sufficient intuitive feel for war to obtain higher success rates and for some of them, like Frederick the Great of Prussia and Napoleon, to offer advice based on these insights. Karl von

Clausewitz's posthumously published *On War* was, on the other hand, the work of a military officer who complemented his own combat experience with prior study of military 'science'. Although not OR as it is known today, it did include theory and observation of behaviours in combat and referred to aspects of this, including fear and bravery, to which we will return later.

A new approach to the study of war was advocated by Count Leon Tolstoi in his classic of the Napoleonic Wars *War and Peace*:

> 'The answers given by historians to the question 'What force moves events?' are satisfactory only so long as each event has but one historian. But so soon as historians of different nationalities and views begin to describe one and the same event, then the answers given by them immediately become nonsensical; since this force is understood by each one of them not merely in a different way but often in an absolutely contradictory way…..
>
> Thus the historians of this class, by mutually destroying each other's position, in the same process destroy its conception of force producing the events, and give no answer to the essential question of history.'

He then continues to criticise general historians and historians of culture, summing up all categories with:

> 'Historical science, at the present time, in its relation to the questions of humanity, is like money in circulation ……..
> Biographies and the ordinary histories of nations are like bank notes. They may pass and circulate, satisfying their denominations without inquiry to any one, and even to be of service, so long as the question does not arise whether their value is assured.'

Rather, he suggests:

> '..instead of seeking for causes, History takes as its problem the search for laws……Along this route all the human sciences have travelled.'

In other words, history itself should be treated more as a science. Even more to the point, as far as OR is concerned, was the rather tongue-in-cheek letter written by Benjamin Franklin to Joseph Priestley in 1775, just after the British pyrrhic victory at the outset of the American War of Independence:

> 'Britain, at the expense of three millions, has killed 150 Yankees this campaign, which is £20,000 a head. And at Bunkers Hill she gained a mile of ground, half of which she lost by our taking post on Ploughed Hill. During the same time 60,000 children have been born in America. From these data any mathematical head will easily calculate the time and expense necessary to kill us all, and conquer our whole territory.'[3]

It was this type of approach which was adopted by two men during World War 1 to develop combat modelling as a means of improving understanding of the mechanics of war. The British engineer F W Lanchester investigated the new phenomenon of aerial warfare, publishing his findings in 1916.[4] The cornerstone of them was the Lanchester N-Squared Law of Combat, which stated that the effective combat power of two forces in conflict with one another is proportional to the effectiveness of their respective weapons times the square of their relative troop strengths. The Russian M Osipov examined land warfare, testing battles over the period 1805-1905, and developed a similar model, although he concluded that the value 3/2 fitted better than the 2 of the 'square law'.[5] Both Lanchester's and Osipov's work have been accepted in their respective spheres and been developed in more sophisticated forms. Some of this type of OR work was pursued by the Royal Naval Air Service, but the thrust of scientific input to defence during 1914-18 was in technical developments such as communications equipment, submarines, tanks and aircraft, and not OR.

Recognising the part that science had played during the war, directors of scientific research were appointed to the Admiralty and Air Ministry in 1919 and 1924 respectively, while the War Office eventually took the same step in 1938. It was, however, the Air Ministry which took the lead in establishing OR as a vital branch of military science. The origins lay in the development of radar in the years leading up to World War 2. The driving force behind it, Robert Watson-Watt, was posted as Superintendent of the Bawdsey Research Station on the Suffolk coast and in 1936 he began to develop the necessary fighter interception techniques which would be required to defeat an air attack on Britain. Much of the work involved practical exercises with RAF Fighter Command and concerned the need for the speedy passage of accurate and relevant information from the radar stations themselves. During the 1938 air exercises the term 'operational research' was actually used to describe this type of trial. Further details on the early British experience with Operational Research have recently been recounted by Kirby.[6,7]

Then, in mid 1940, a group of scientists who had been involved with defence matters published an anonymous manifesto *Science in War*.[8] Among them were men who would soon become household names – Professors P M S Blackett, J D Bernal, S Zuckerman, and C H Waddington. They made the point that so far the scientific effort had been directed towards technological improvements in weapons and equipment.

> 'Yet the use of these weapons and the organisation of the men who handle them are at least as much scientific problems as their production. The waging of warfare represents a series of human operations carried out for more or less definite ends. Seeing whether these operations actually yield the results expected from them should be a matter of direct scientific analysis. The ultimate answer is provided by victory or defeat, but the failure to understand the factors contributing to that victory or defeat, and the degree to which each contributes, removes any secure ground for organising further success …
>
> It is possible to reduce many of the factors in military operations to numerical values. Doing so provides problems capable of definite solution … The scientific staffs of the Services need to play a much larger part than they seem to do in the formulation and solution of strategical and tactical problems.'

Not only did this statement crystallise the value of military OR, and, indeed, that in other OR fields as well, it also galvanised action at the time. By the end of 1940, scientists were attached to the principal RAF operational commands in the UK. The Royal Navy, too, also established OR sections (ORS). The Army was more hesitant, but Professor Blackett was able to form a section to provide Anti-Aircraft Command in Britain with advice.

Initially, it was the RAF which continued to make the running in OR. In Fighter Command much work continued in improving the reporting system so as to make the fighters more responsive. OR also played its part in the development of an Identification Friend or Foe (IFF) system, as well as that of effective night fighting techniques and establishing that aircraft maintenance was more efficiently carried out by a larger rather than smaller team of fitters. Bomber Command was slower off the mark and it was only after its complacency was severely shaken by the summer 1941 Butt Report, which revealed from an analysis of air photographs how woefully inaccurate its night bombing was, that it began to turn to science to assist it.

The Bomber Command ORS was established in September 1941 'for the purpose of analysing bombing operations with a view to determining weak points in the enemy defence system, to ascertain the cause of casualties so that steps can be taken to reduce them and to assess the effectiveness of bombing attacks. The section will also be investigating various radio problems relating to this Command.'[9] One of its early successes was 'streaming'. The practice had been for the bombers to attack a target in small groups over a period of time. Using the theory that each German radar could only direct fighters on to one bomber at a time, the ORS developed a technique, whereby ten bombers would pass a given point every minute, which also provided for a more concentrated attack and better use of surprise. The main concern of the airmen was that of mid-air collisions, but the ORS was able to establish mathematically that the risk was considerably less than being shot down by enemy fire. The first real opportunity to test the concept came at the end of May 1942 with the first 1,000 bomber raid mounted by the RAF, its target Cologne. Dr Basil Dickins, the head of the Bomber Command ORS, correctly forecast that there would be just one collision. Furthermore, the overall bomber losses on the raid were considerably less than feared. The ORS also did much to perfect the techniques for the new navigation aids – Gee, H2S, and others. Radio counter-measures were another area on which it concentrated.

The Coastal Command ORS was particularly concerned with the war against the U-boat. The initial trigger was the development of Air to Surface Vessel (ASV) radar, which became one of the key elements in the campaign. However, visual detection of U-boats was just as important. The ORS established that 66 per cent of U-boats spotted the aircraft before it saw the submarine and so were able to evade attack. One way of overcoming this was camouflage. At the time, Coastal Command aircraft were painted black as a defence against searchlights, but the ORS concluded that those operating away from possible searchlights should have their bellies and sides painted white, with 'dark sea grey' being used over seas like the Mediterranean, where there was bright sunlight. According to Professor C H Waddington, who worked in the Coastal Command ORS before becoming the scientific adviser to the AOCinC Coastal Command for the last three years of the war, this, together with improved sighting arrangements for the aircraft look-outs, resulted in the number of evading U-boats reducing from 66 per cent to some 20 per cent.[10] When it came to attacking U-boats, it was the ORS which established the optimum setting for aerially delivered depth charges, resulting in a significant increase in the number of U-boats sunk. These were just a few of the measures which resulted in aircraft being able to claim over 50 per cent of the total U-boat 'kills' during the war.

Naval OR was also much concerned with the war against the U-boat. It was able to establish that larger merchant convoys were a more effective defence and also helped to develop standard drills by escort vessels for attacking U-boats threatening convoys. Indeed, OR could be said to have played a major role in turning the Battle of the Atlantic from impending defeat to impending victory by the end of May 1943, when Grand Admiral Karl Doenitz was forced to temporarily withdraw his U-boats because of the heavy casualties they had suffered during that month. Yet, while Professor Blackett was invited by the Admiralty in 1942 to form the Naval OR branch and become its director, the honeymoon was relatively short-lived. Solly Zuckerman noted in 1944:

> 'I was sad to learn that civilian advisers were out of favour. Blackett, who had helped enormously at the start of the war in showing how anti-aircraft fire should be used, and who was now the best-known scientist in the Admiralty, was in evidence in Portsmouth, but somehow or other he was no longer in good odour with his naval colleagues. He never attended any of our meetings and when I asked why, Kingston told me that he was, in fact, being denied access to the War Room. It seemed incredible that this could have happened to the man who, if anyone deserved the description, was the father of Operational Research.'[11]

Given the valuable work that both Naval OR and that connected with RAF Coastal Command, which was under the operational control of the Admiralty, had done and were doing, it was an unfortunate situation.

Apart from Blackett's early work with Anti-Aircraft (AA) Command, which was primarily concerned with radar, Army OR was slow to get off the ground. Not until May 1942 was a scientific adviser, Sir Charles Darwin, appointed, and his belief that there should be independent scientific observation of battles 'to establish facts to replace opinions' initially fell on stony ground. Indeed, the Army did not like the 'operational' in OR because it seemed to imply that scientists wanted to dictate tactics. Thus, an Army Council Secretariat paper written in July 1942 on the setting up of an Army OR Group (AORG) stated:

> '… the object of the Group will be to study current events and equipment in the field with the purpose of showing how improvements could be made in the materiel, in the technique of its use and the tactical employment of technical troops. It is not required to study original future developments or military tactics as such.'[12]

Apart from AA, Army OR was initially concerned with coastal defence and early warning, which again involved radar, the jamming of radio communications, and tank gunnery. But the worm did turn. Like the RAF, the Army did deploy OR sections to the theatres of war. That sent to South East Asia Command was headed by Brigadier J D Welch. In a lecture given to the Army Staff College in September 1945,[13] he gave an illuminating feel for the role of OR. His brief was to 'study tactics, organisation, weapons and equipment and to make recommendations.' He was also to 'consider the application of inventions and new devices to jungle warfare'. One of his approaches was to carry out a casualty study so as to identify the most effective jungle weapons. Military efficiency, including how to lay pipelines, was another subject he found himself tackling. The importance of trials, which was one of AORG's remits, was a further field in which his team became deeply involved. He found that new equipments were given to field formations to test, but the troops were often too busy to make any sound judgement. Indeed, he cited the example of a hand-cart which was trialled for use in the Burma jungle.

> 'All formations replied that they did not want them except a West African division who answered that they were very good but the axle was too far forward. Investigations showed that the West African troops had been carrying them on their heads.'

It reinforced the point that equipment trials could only be meaningful if they were properly supervised.

Other very good work was performed by No 2 ORS with 21st Army Group in North-West Europe during 1944-45. Their collected reports have recently been published by Terry Copp.[14] Montgomery had not been overly enthusiastic about OR when his was commanding Eighth Army in North Africa. A section had been sent out to him, but it was forbidden to enter the battle area. An OR officer, without staff, deployed with First Army in Tunisia and experienced similar treatment. Both sections were then merged and then disbanded in April 1943. A fresh section was sent to Eighth Army in Italy, but was again frustrated and had to content itself mainly with investigations into artillery performance and AFV mobility. Indeed, it was thanks only to Professor C D Ellis, who had taken over from Darwin as scientific adviser to the Army Council and who personally negotiated with Montgomery, that No 2 ORS was allowed to go to Normandy. Placed in charge of the section was Colonel Basil Schonland, an established South African scientist who had joined OR in 1941 while across in Britain to procure radars for his own army. To give him sufficient status he was promoted Brigadier and allowed direct access to Montgomery's Chief of Staff, Freddie de Guingand.

The first member of No 2 ORS landed in Normandy on D-Day itself and spent the next three weeks helping to perfect the AA defences in the beachhead. Thereafter the Section carried out a number of studies, producing over forty reports by the end of the war. They included an investigation of the effects of air and naval bombardment on the German coast defences in Normandy and a number of studies on the effects of carpet bombing by RAF Bomber Command on German field defences prior to an attack. In the latter case, the conclusion was that the morale effect on German combat effectiveness far outweighed the influence of the physical destruction of weapons and equipment and the infliction of casualties. A reflection of a growing concern among the high command was a study of infantry officer casualties. The ORS was, however, unable to come up with any firm conclusions over how they could be reduced, apart from improved training and more reliable communications. Other reports encompassed the effects of artillery fire on German morale, tank casualties, and mortar location. One particularly interesting study, in which No 2 ORS worked with its RAF equivalent, concerned the German counterstroke into the flank of the US breakout at Mortain in August 1944. The general belief in both the RAF and USAAF was that it was fighter-bombers armed with rockets which had halted the attack. Indeed, American and British pilots claimed over 300 vehicles definitely destroyed. The OR sections were able to inspect the battlefield very shortly after the action and located 78 knocked out tanks among other destroyed vehicles. Of these, 27 per cent had been knocked out by aircraft and some 17 per cent abandoned or destroyed by their crews, indicating the morale effect of the air attacks. Of the remainder, 37 per cent had been destroyed by the ground troops and the cause of the loss of the remainder could not be established. Thus, it would seem that aircraft and ground forces contributed in equal measure.[15]

Fig 1.1
Army Operational
Research Group
Sections

Back in Britain, Army OR had expanded into numerous fields, which are best described by the use of a table:

Section	Sub-Section	Function
AORS 1 Air Defence Radar	1a (AA Command and School of Artillery)	Performance of a modification to standard service Radar Equipment in AA and FA Roles
	1b AA Command	AA & SL Operations and Equipment trials
	1c (Air Defence Division, SHAEF)	Analysis of Continental V-weapon operations
AORS 2 Coastal Radar	2a (Coast Defences [CD])	Performance of CD and CA Sets; Study of Anomalous Propagation
and Gunnery	2b (Coast Artillery [CA] Units)	Analysis of CA Shoots and Trials
AORS 3 Signals		Signals problems and performance of signals equipment in the field
AORS 4 AFV Field A/TK Artillery	4a (Gunnery Wing; AFV School)	AFV Gunnery, Tank Mobility and Tactical Problems
	4b (School of Artillery)	A/Tk & FA trials and problems
AORS 5 Airborne Forces	Army Airborne Transport Development centre.	Equipment and Exercises of Airborne Forces
AORS 6 Infantry	Infantry Battle School	Infantry Weapons and Tactics
AORS 7 Lethality of Weapons	7a	General mathematical problems, Fragmentation and Fuzes
	7b	Accuracy and Lethality of Artillery Fire, Field Trials and Exercises

THE STRESS OF BATTLE

Section	Sub-Section	Function
AORS 8 Problems of New Equipment	8a	Mines and Obstacles
	8c	Special optical aids and visual problems
	8d	Flame Throwers and Smoke
AORS 9 Time and Motion Studies		Time and Motion Studies of drill and uses of equipment
AORS 10 Battle Analysis		Analysis of Battle Records
Library Publication		Publication of Reports and Memoranda
Photographic Liaison Section		Circulation of information

Fig 1.1 Army Operational Research Group Sections (*continued*)

Adapted from R W Shephard, ed. *Readings on Early Military Operational Research (With Particular Reference to Army OR)14* (Shrivenham, England: Royal Military College of Science 1984), p 97.

Military OR can be said to have come of age during World War 2. Its use had been demonstrated over a wide range of topics, especially in the more effective use of existing weapons and the development of new ones. A notable feature of the wartime OR scientists was the variety of disciplines from which they were drawn. In addition to physicians and mathematicians, still well represented in OA, there were also zoologists (such as Professor Zuckerman), physiologists and geneticists. This breadth was recognised as a positive feature in giving diversity to this fast developing area of scientific research. Zuckerman himself wrote: 'Operational problems, I discovered, savoured more of the characteristics of biological enquiry than those encountered by chemists and physicists.'[16] It was this breadth of knowledge and experience, often without preconceived ideas as far as military matters were concerned, which so often produced the lateral thought needed to solve what at the time appeared to be intractable problems.

Recognition of the achievements of OR was reflected in the fact that the Armed Services continued with their own OR branches after the war. The Army's AORG settled into a country house at Broadoaks, West Byfleet in Surrey. One element of it was, however, separated from AORG and became the Army Personnel Research Establishment (APRE) at Farnborough. In 1965, following the establishment of a unified Ministry of Defence the previous year, the Army Operational Research Establishment (as AORG had become) was absorbed into a new tri-service Defence Operational Analysis Establishment (DOAE), which took over the Broadoaks site. The reason for the change from Operational Research to Analysis was to avoid confusion with the Operational Requirements (OR) function, which had its own single service directorates within the Ministry of Defence and was responsible for drawing up the specifications for new weapons and equipment. Broadoaks remained the centre for tri-service OA until 1996, when the High-Level Studies Department of the Centre for Defence Analysis, as DOAE had become, moved to Farnborough.

Former Offices of Defence Operational Analysis Establishment at West Byfleet.

Over the post-war period the nature of OA changed in several ways. While it includes, as an applied science, the techniques

THE STRESS OF BATTLE

of observation, analysis, the formulation of hypotheses, and experimentation, much of the World War 2 work relied mainly on observation and quick analysis, with the possibility of experiment through field exercises or observation of combat. In peacetime, however, combat is infrequent and the resources to test in field conditions are less. There was, too, the spectre of nuclear war, of which, apart from the dropping of the A-bombs on Japan in August 1945, there was no practical experience. As Dr R A Forder has written[17]:

> 'In many key areas, analysis based on accumulated operational and trials data was of limited value. Yet military planners too found their own operational experience of rather limited value, so they were still keen to call up the scientific advice which had proved so valuable in war. But the scientific advice would have to be of a different sort. Rather than making sense of real, day-to-day operations, analysts now had to be concerned with hypothetical circumstances, hypothetical enemy reactions and the pros and cons of equipment as yet unprocured, perhaps even undeveloped.'

The 'New Wing' of the former DOAE offices at West Byfleet.

To provide a mechanism for developing the necessary hypotheses, the analysts began to utilise the war game, a traditional method of training commanders and developing strategy and tactics. The effectiveness of this tool was significantly increased by the introduction of the computer, which, indeed, transformed it. Forder again:

> 'The advent of powerful computers was certainly the single greatest influence on OA in the 1960s and 70s. They were used for many types of calculation and modelling, but it was in supporting simulation where the effect was greatest. Reliance on large computer simulations may not always have been very comfortable for analysts, but they filled an important 'market need'. They still do. They allowed the analyst to break free from the constraints of other approaches to combat assessments; purely analytical formulations were only applicable to the most aggregated or stylised situations; firepower indices and other force scoring methods neglected the dynamics of battle; war-games could not produce consistent and reproducible quantitative results. The ability to produce large combat simulations also matched the problems that analysts were called upon to tackle in the late 1960s [as] NATO moved away from the doctrine of massive retaliation to that of flexible response and this put more emphasis on looking in detail at big conventional wars.'[17]

The type of investigation carried out by DOAE included such subjects as the optimum weapons mix in various given situations, deployment postures, decision making, and likely ammunition expenditure.

This is not to say that other OA methods were abandoned. OA teams were deployed during some of the post-war campaigns. One was present during the Korean War and wrote a number of reports, covering topics ranging from personal protection (helmets, winter clothing and body armour, to geography and climate and the employment of tanks). The OR Unit Far East did some very valuable work during the Malayan Emergency, monitoring operations and providing advice based on extensive analysis. The same unit, although much reduced in size, also provided input during the Confrontation with Indonesia in Borneo during 1963-66. The analysts from the Field Studies Group within AORG and DOAE were also able to conduct a number of field trials involving troops, from which useful data was obtained. One example of this was Exercise Helltank, which culminated in 1967 with a brigade-sized exercise in Germany. Its purpose was to investigate the employment of anti-tank helicopters. The military historian Major Kenneth Macksey took part as a member of the Field Studies Group and concluded:

> 'Nobody who witnessed that exercise was left in doubt that the helicopter-armed or otherwise – had a future as a complementary part of the existing system. But it was also clear that, like all other weapon systems, the helicopter needed to be integrated with other forces and could not rush, willy-nilly, about the battlefield as if possessed with an inbuilt invulnerability. By the same token, it was also appreciated that ground forces themselves could not longer behave with impunity in the face of this new threat.'[18]

Yet, unless firmly based on studies of actual combat, such tools as war gaming, computer simulation, mathematical modelling, and field exercises were and are often unable to provide a complete answer. The reason for this is that they cannot realistically identify what actually happens during a battle. This was something recognised by the World War 2 analysts when examining recently fought over battlefields, as No 2 ORS noted in Normandy:

> 'The lack of knowledge of what had really happened in battle, that prompted our first investigation of the bombing of Caen, turned out to be the root cause of almost all the work we subsequently did. This ignorance was not of the sort that might, for instance, prompt such a question as: how can factory chimneys be knocked down by air or artillery? Though we were sometimes given such problems, they were usually referred to technical experts in the theatre or at home.'

'Rather was it ignorance of a less technical and more
fundamental nature which arose from the vastness and
impersonality of modern warfare, where the end-results of
a particular course of action are quite remote from the
initiators; where, for instance, the results of air attack on an
enemy position can only be judged by whether the subsequent
ground attack succeeded, when in fact it may have succeeded
for a dozen other reasons. In consequence, our work developed
into the search for means to reconstruct and analyse particular
battles. Once the missing elements of the battle had been
supplied, suggestions for improvement followed; once for
instance, the real value of a particular air attack had been
determined, it was not difficult to say whether another type
of attack would have been better.'[19]

The report went on to emphasise that OR 'is much more than the
straightforward collection of facts and the writing of histories; it
must continually seek out all the sources of information, especially
the least obvious, and, by sound reasoning from the facts, provide
a new understanding of its particular problem.'[19]

One of the elements implied in the report was the human factor,
of which modelling, simulation, and even field exercises took little
account. As will be recounted, it was this that caused Historical
Analysis (HA) to become a significant tool in OA. Yet, in spite of
the mass of historical data which had been accumulated on past
campaigns through war diaries, after action reports, and the like,
it had been largely ignored in the years after 1945. Much of the
reason for this was the belief that nuclear warfare was a totally
new environment to which past 'conventional' warfare had little
relevance. Furthermore, the development of new weapons systems
like the guided weapon could not, it was thought, be equated to
those used previously in combat. In addition, it was considered
that the variety of conditions in which combat occurred,
combined with the outcome of superficially similar situations,
meant that useful results were unlikely to be obtained. This, as
will be seen, proved not to be so.

The starting point for historical analysis began with DOAE's Field Studies Division, whose role was to provide data and advice for the creation of models and wargames. Its work included field trials to examine tactical interactions and deployments. However, the tactical basis for such studies was not interactive; prior plans were examined without taking account of, the effect of one side's fire or movement on the other. Since it was accepted that exercise conditions were very different to those in actual combat, apart from the obvious differences, the fact that casualty infliction was in the hands of umpires, who could only give a subjective view, meant that data obtained was likely to be very unreliable.

The advent of pulsed laser weapons simulators in the 1970s did overcome some of these problems, enabling engagements to take place in near real time and for 'battles' to flow without pauses for umpire interventions.

DOAE was able to take advantage of these simulators, enabling the identification of many additional aspects of combat which needed representation in combat modelling and in real life battle planning, eg the effects of fire control problems causing overkill, and realistic tactical rates of fire being less than in range firing and varying with number of targets. In addition to this, as the exercises progressed, the analysis and its application also led to further consideration of the differences between such exercise conditions and conflict in real war. In time this led consideration back again to real combat through the study of history, but now with important differences.

Study of historical combat could now be approached with the background of analysis of several series of interactive combat exercises. These provided several important benchmarks which brought extra order to the study of history. The three main aspects covered were:

a. The variability of combat, even in the same conditions (eg same troops and same equipment on the same ground). This is due to differences in time to detect targets, to chance events in killing targets and to the cumulative effects of such events, all of which would also apply in real life. Thus an estimated threshold (or lower limit) value of variability became available for certain basic combat situations.

b. The overall value of a force's lethality, as it engaged an enemy, was now assessable from exercises. These represented all the real world problems of meeting forces except, of course, for the live fire elements and their consequences.

c. The form of relationships between casualty infliction and target availability (as force ratio) was now assessable from exercise data, providing an avenue into the hitherto intransigent problems of historical data analysis.

The combined effects of these three aspects now made the analysis of historical combat data feasible for the equivalent combat situations. This was explored initially for small arms fire at personnel targets for which there has been less technical change over the years than, for example, for armour and anti-armour weapons.

From this start and the consistency and robustness of its results, together with the lessons learnt in the process, it became possible to expand historical analysis to more complicated situations and to examine many aspects of the effects of live fire on combat behaviour and effectiveness. In particular, it proved possible to quantify the human factor in battle in terms of 'combat degradation', which is defined as the difference between physically realistic exercise behaviour and that in the equivalent live fire battles.

Given that the exercise/trials phase provided a key link in the process and itself unearthed many aspects of combat behaviour to be considered, these will described with examples. Following this, successive chapters deal with the initial exercises: combat comparison for small arms then the more complicated armour - anti-armour case which had to make different use of the corresponding exercises. The whole process involved the setting up, observation and subsequent analysis of several hundred exercise battles of simulated combat, the reading-up and analysis of many hundreds more of real battles with the support of dedicated historians, meeting key individuals who had fought in some, and finding that the main variations can be reconciled by identifiable aspects of behaviour when under the extreme conditions of danger in combat.

It is, however, important to distinguish Historical Analysis from 'history' itself. While history forms the major input into historical analysis, it is the objective data derived from it which is the important part. Historians' judgements and views are also useful but as hypotheses to test and not as direct input. The analysis itself also takes into account hypotheses in the form of doctrine and principles developed from Military Studies, as well as those, when it comes to human factors, from the field of psychology. The historical analysis can then be used for operational research, as shown in Figure 1.2 below:

Figure 1.2
Diagrammatic
Representation of
the Interaction with
Historical Analysis

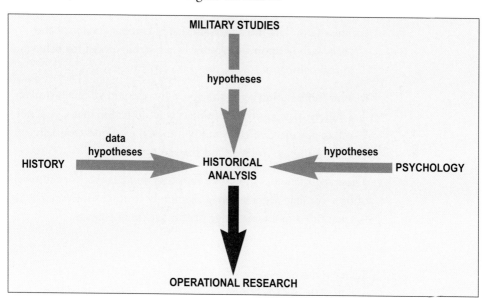

In other words, three areas provide inputs, while OR uses the output to test hypotheses in order to develop as a science.

In order to do this effectively there is a requirement for:

a. The recognition of the value of interaction by those working in the four adjacent areas, which sometimes interact as individual pairs, but seldom as a broad team.

b. The need for appropriate historical data in the form of accounts with full data banks compiled at varying levels of detail. These are required at all levels of combat, from platoon or individual weapon level up to army operations, and should include the tabulation of possibly relevant factors but avoid the assignment of causes, except as hypotheses.

c. The formulation of hypotheses capable of test by the data, by psychologists who study behaviour under fear and in stressed situations.

d. The use of military doctrine and principles, restated as hypotheses to test, and an awareness that this type of study will not always yield the answers expected. Two examples, concerning the anti-armour battle and urban warfare, are discussed in the book.

e. The use of data from field simulated combat (exercises and trials with weapon simulators) as a testable model for behaviour in real combat.

f. The combination of all the above by operational analysts from a variety of scientific disciplines, who do realise that OA is not yet an advanced science and will treat it cautiously, initially attempting to structure and then to quantify it.

These requirements should be borne in mind as the story unravels of how combat degradation, a seemingly abstract subject, came to be quantified in a wide range of combat circumstances.

Source Notes

[1] *Air Ministry The Origins and Development of Operational Research in the RAF* HMSO, London, 1963

[2] Defence Operational Analysis Establishment information booklet, 1984

[3] Quoted Jones, R V *Most Secret War* p208 Wordsworth Paperback edition, Ware, 1998

[4] *Aircraft in Warfare: The Dawn of the Fourth Arm* Constable, London, 1916

[5] Helmbold, Dr R L *Osipov: The Russian Lanchester* US Army CAA Paper, 1989

[6] Kirby, M W: *Early Operations Research in World War One: Viscount Tiverton and the Strategic Bombing of Germany* Military Operations research, 9,2,5-15 (2004)

[7] Kirby, M W: *Operational Research in War and peace: The British Experience from the 1930s to 1970* Imperial College Press London (2003)

[8] Published as a Penguin paperback

[9] Air Ministry op cit p44

[10] Waddington, Prof C H *OR in World War 2: Operational Research Against the U-Boat* p158 Elek Science, London, 1973

[11] Zuckerman, Solly *From Apes to Warlords* p266 Hamish Hamilton, London, 1978

[12] National Archives, Kew WO 32/10574

[13] Ibid WO 203/718

[14] Copp, Terry(ed) *Montgomery's Scientists: Operational Research in Northwest Europe: The Work of No2 Operational Research Section with 21 Army Group, June 1944 to July 1945* Waterloo, Ontario: Laurier Centre for Military Strategic & Disarmament Studies, Wilfirid Laurier Univ, Waterloo, Ontario, Canada, 2000.

[15] Ibid WO 106/4348

[16] Zuckerman op cit p363

[17] Forder R A *Operational Analysis in Defence: A Retrospect* presented at NATO Partnership for Peace Symposium on " *The Applications of Operations Analysis to Defence Decision making*" held at Garmisch Partenkirchen, Germany 2000

[18] Macksey, Maj Kenneth MC RTR (Retd) *The Tanks: A History of the Royal Tank Regiment, 1945-1975* p178 Arms and Armour, London, 1979

[19] WO 106/4348 op cit

CHAPTER TWO
From Field Trials to Historical Analysis

One of the organisations which DOAE inherited from AORG, was the Field Studies Division. Included in this was the Field Trials Group, a practical and flexible trials organisation, able to monitor military deployments and behaviour in the field on exercises, and to collect, reduce and analyse the data so obtained. Although the balance of studies was heavily weighted to Army operations because of its historical attachment, the division did combat studies for all three Services. Some of the main themes of study had included:

a. Target detection (visual and with radar and night vision devices).

b. Intervisibility, the limitations to line of sight between two sides caused by terrain screening.

c. Tactical use of anti-tank helicopters (on field training exercises).

d. The effectiveness of smoke in battlefield obscuration.

e. Fighter Ground Attack (FGA) detection of ground targets.

The Field Trials Group carried out combat trials, data reduction and basic analysis, reporting its findings direct to the sponsor of the trial. The 'studies' part of the Division provided a complementary capability. It designed trials for specific purposes, interpreted and analysed their results and, in order to obtain the maximum value from DOAE trials, carried out supplementary analysis and comparison with other trials. Thus the role of the 'studies' team was to transform the practical study of the processes of combat into an empirical science for the users - military HQs and combat modellers - ensuring that the best long-term value was obtained from the expensive effort of the field trials.

The Field Trials Group studies themselves were sometimes based on fairly 'clinical' situations, using small groups of men and equipment provided by the Services for the trial. Others monitored Field

Training Exercises (FTXs). While these enabled realistic deployments to be studied, their value was limited by the fact that the exercises were scripted to meet training requirements. A further source was the TEWT or Tactical Exercise Without Troops, which involved commanders at all levels considering tactical problems on the ground. While all three methods provided useful data, much of that pertaining to actual combat lacked objectivity, especially when it came to casualty assessments.

However, in the early 1970s a new training aid was introduced, Simfire. Initially designed to be fitted to AFVs, it was later adapted for individual infantrymen. In essence, it consisted of a laser 'gun' which was fired from the tank. Sensors mounted on the target vehicle would indicate a 'hit' and would trigger the detonation of an orange smoke canister. The firing of the laser also simulated the flash and smoke of the actual main armament being fired.

Diagrammatically, Simfire functioned as shown below:

Figure 2.1
SIMFIRE System Operation

WITH ACKNOWLEDGEMENT TO WESTON SIMFIRE

Gunner fires.
Auto range to target measurement.
Projector depression set to cancel tangent elevation.
Bang generation by blank ammunition, or as required.

Target responds by repeating interrogation on radio link.

Projector interrogates for +/−/L/R/direct hit state.
Signals lay error to gunner & commander.

Target responds by repeating interrogation on radio link.

Control system evaluates kill state as function of range, ammunition type and target category.
Signals kill, if appropriate.

Target decodes kill indication, actuates 'self destruction' i.e. fires smoke generator, de-activates weapon and radio transmission.

What Simfire offered was major step forward in exercise realism, especially in battlefield deployment, target detection and

FROM FIELD TRIALS TO HISTORICAL ANALYSIS 23

DOAE Field Studies Mobile Control and monitoring vehicles deployed for field trial

engagement, and movement. This meant that meaningful interactive combat field trials were now possible.

The initial DOAE involvement in interactive exercises was connected with Anglo-German co-operation on future main battle tank design. Examination of the options led to a practical trial Exercise Dawdle in 1973. This trial included low-level exercises to compare the Swedish 'S' Tank with the British Army's Chieftain tank as part of the investigation into a possible turretless tank design. Two squadrons, each equipped with one tank type, took part, and one phase compared low-level interactive battles at squadron/troop level, using Simfire.

Chieftain and (loaned) S-Tank of 2RTR on Exercise DAWDLE, which included simple interactive exercises using SIMFIRE

Exercise Chinese Eye

The successful use of Simfire on the S Tank exercise led to a proposal for a more ambitious data collection exercise using simulated armoured battles. This exercise or trial emerged as Exercise Chinese Eye. The regiment nominated for the role, 4th Royal Tank Regiment (4RTR), selected the name.[*]

Chinese Eye was set up to simulate a series of armoured combat actions between two forces, one following British mobile defence tactics and the other employing those typical of the Warsaw Pact. Each action used a fresh area of terrain. The actions took place over a selection of terrain representing that of the 1(BR) Corps area, mainly farmland south of Hanover in Germany. Most of the weapon systems were represented by Simfire, thus allowing a high degree of tactical realism.

Twenty separate actions, including an initial practice run, were fought during November 1975 between two standard forces:

a. BLUE combat team in defence, comprising two troops of four Chieftain tanks each, a notional mechanised infantry platoon, two sections each of one Swingfire anti-tank guided weapon system (ATGW) (totalling two launchers), a MILAN ATGW section (four launchers) and an additional two tanks representing the combat team HQ.

b. ORANGE tank battalion in attack, comprising three tank companies (Chieftains as surrogate T-62s), each with ten tanks, a motor rifle company and a headquarters group.

The detailed orders of battle are shown overleaf:

Actions were limited to direct fire engagements, but each side did prepare artillery plans. Minefields were represented and their effect simulated by umpiring. Each scenario lasted 30-60 minutes, but

---

[*] The name embodied the insignia of 4RTR, a lucky Chinese Eye painted on their tank turrets in recognition of the original gift of a tank to the Tank Corps in World War I by a wealthy Chinese member of the Federal Council of Malaya.

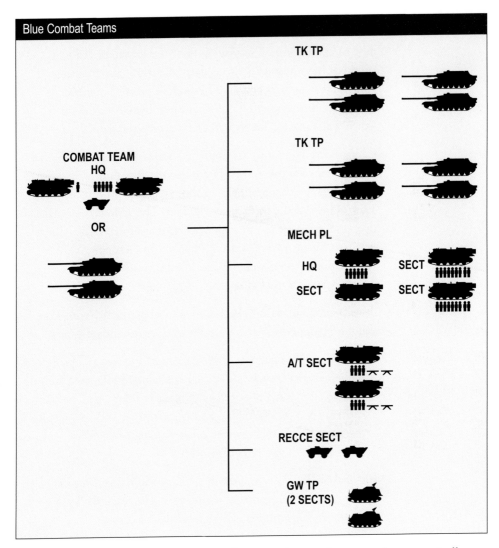

Figure 2.2
ORBATS

the time of contact between the two forces was lower, typically about 20 minutes.

The odds in favour of ORANGE were 3:1 in tanks or 2:1 in tank and anti-tank weapons. All tanks were equipped with Simfire and thunderflashes were used to represent missile launch signatures. Simkill, the Simfire target kit, was fitted to the FV432 armoured personnel carriers, with which the attack infantry were equipped, and also to the FV438 Swingfire vehicles. Tank kills were

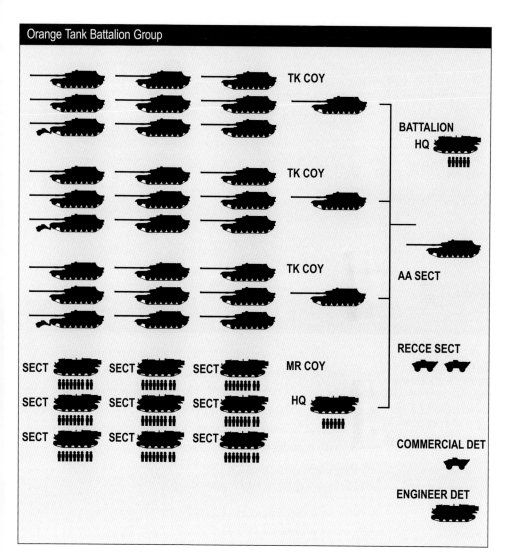

represented by the Simfire orange smoke pyrotechnic. Furthermore, killed tanks elevated their tank guns and switched on a flashing orange light mounted on the turret. These further measures compensated for the unrealistic situation which would have existed as a result of leaving undestroyed tanks with no distinguishing features, such as obvious damage or smoke. The tanks on each side began each action with notional British and Warsaw Pact standard ammunition loads – 48 main armament rounds for the Chieftains and 40 for the 'T-62s'.

A 4RTR tank on Ex CHINESE EYE. All the Chieftains were fitted with SIMFIRE as shown (projector on gun barrel and detectors around turret)

Artillery and smoke were not represented on the ground, since their neutralisation and obscurant effects could neither be physically created nor measured. However, their planned use was recorded. A Forward Observation Officer (FOO) was attached to BLUE and he recorded requests for fire support. Similarly, a battery commander was attached to ORANGE and he recorded fire plans and calls for fire support. The data for each side's artillery was analysed and reported separately.

A range of complementary data collection systems were used for each weapon system:

a. A log book of activities maintained by crew members.

b. Debrief forms completed immediately after each action.

c. Taped records, against time, of radio nets, tank intercoms and of Simfire function.

Of these three sources, the third was undoubtedly the most comprehensive and reliable. Transcripts of the taped records provided data for the bulk of analysis. In the occasional absence of taped records, due mainly to recorder failure in the tank, log books and debrief forms were scrutinised. In addition, these sometimes amplified or explained the tape-recorded data.

Additional data collection included the use of air photographs from a helicopter overflying the exercise area. These, supported by a running commentary, provided positional data at certain times and also showed tank tracks between these times which, combined with tank intercom tapes, allowed detailed time and position serials to be compiled. Central recording of each side's battle nets, in addition to the helicopter observer net, allowed the overall tactical situation and its interpretation by both sides to be monitored. A further photographic source was provided by time lapse panoramas from cameras at extra positions in each tank troop's area of deployment, allowing sample target arrays to be studied.

Taped records were transcribed and the time associated with each message was noted. Simultaneously with this, the time associated with Simfire functions - tank firing, tank under attack, tank killed - were also noted, since each different function created an electronic impulse, registered as an audible tone on the tank tape. These lengthy transcripts were then summarised to eliminate unnecessary information and to highlight the time, duration and content of key events, messages, and instructions between crew members.

Details of events other than the actual firing, e.g. range of shot, time of firing etc, could be accurately associated with taped records for approximately 1,700 rounds out of the 2,741 fired. This sample provided the main source for the analyses. Data on targets of other firings could be deduced from reconstructions.

A series of data banks was then constructed by coding the information for the computer at DOAE. The prime bank of 30,000 elements contained the information relating to each individual round that was fired. This comprised the tank's radio callsign, scenario number, tank survival state, time of firing, degree of voice procedure adopted, estimated range, use of gun traverse, mention of target direction, mention of any detection aid, and target serial number associated with this round. A second bank of 17,000 elements stored details of the time that each part of a fire order was issued as well as the times that stop and start commands were given. Two further data banks stored the times that 'under attack' and 'killed' signals were emitted by each tank's Simfire kit.

Results from Analysis of Ex Chinese Eye

An interim period of data reduction and analysis followed, leading to the production of a series of reports on the broad areas of 'movement and tactics', 'intervisibility' and 'weapon engagements', and supplementing memoranda and working papers on the analyses. In addition, a further stage of study allowed the majority of the 19 non-practice scenarios to be reconstructed as detailed histories to aid more detailed analysis. A series of reports covered these, with detailed time records and time sequenced snapshot maps of each side as the battles developed. Two of these reports were subsequently adapted and produced as instructional films and videos.

Figure 2.3 (*opposite*) Factors shown up by Tactical Trials to be More or Less Important than had been assumed by Desk Study

In terms of findings, some significant differences were found between assumptions made, even with military advice, for combat modelling and what transpired during Chinese Eye. These are tabulated in figure 2.3 opposite.

One of the more significant findings concerned intervisibility. In terms of modelling this had been regarded as simply the ability of one target to see another and vice versa and the effect of this was represented as slowing down the attrition battle. Such a representation is adequate if military encounters were simply random occurrences between individual moving weapons and isolated defenders. Yet, both the defence and the attack try to use their forces in a structured manner, which is anything but random. The defence attempts to ensure that its sector of responsibility is covered by surveillance and that the main avenues of approach are covered by sufficient direct fire weapons to thwart an attack. The attack will probe alternative routes and aim to achieve a significantly superior force ratio along those approaches judged most promising. Consequently, the trial recognised that the one-on-one concept was too simplistic and had to incorporate the

THE STRESS OF BATTLE

Subject	Assumed Factors shown by Tactical Trials to be either of less importance than assumed or to be qualified by other factors	Other Important Factors neglected in modelling until shown up by tactical trials
Defence open fire range	Intervisibility and target detection	Fire control
Minimum combat range	Defence decide to withdraw	Unexpected close range encounters and over-runs
Rate of attack closing	Slow due to attackers' decisions and tactics	Fast if following WP tactics
Defence redeployment	As required in battle	Difficult to achieve satisfactorily in face of fast closing attack
Poor visibility	Causes short range battle as attack closes with defence	Also allows attack to penetrate defence positions without engagement
Individual contributions	(Not considered)	Importance of mistakes and misunderstandings. Wide variations in individual contributions
Outcome of battle	Casualties Exchange ratios	Ability of attack to penetrate or locally over-run the defence
Effects of Inter-visibility	Reduce rates of fire and maximum range in large scale battle	To divide battle into separate small engagements
Reasons for defence weapons jockeying	To reduce vulnerability after firing	To allow improved opportunities for engagement, and to avoid being overrun
Defence rate of fire	Cyclic rate of fire limits, Intervisibility and Jockeying	Target detection and selection, too - a function of targets in view
Accuracy of defence fire	Proof and range firing performance	Degradation in accuracy in combat situation
Overkill	Possible constant factor of wasted rounds	Overkill due to lack of fire control, varies with total fire relative to target force
Attack knowledge of defence	Known defence positions leading to small search areas	Unknown defence positions, difficult to predict or detect
Accuracy of attack fire	Only accurate pinpoints engaged	Few pinpoints accurate, many inaccurate engaged
Defence vulnerability	Most defence can obtain hull-down positions	Many defence in hull-up positions although with low visual contrast and detectability

correlation between each side's groups of weapons, and the relative deployments in terms of terrain parameters, especially the degree of ground coverage that they gave. Hence, when this major inter-active armoured trial was planned, so too were supplementary intervisibility studies to collect this force-on-force terrain-deployment data. These surveys provided many interesting descriptions for analysis and comparison for a variety of terrain and deployments.

Figure 2.4 (*opposite*) Relationship of Engagements in Armour/Anti-Armour Battles

In particular, we found that each main 'battle' between the attacking battalion and defending combat team occurred as a set of identifiable mini battles with the individual force ratios (attack strength divided by defence strength) log-normally distributed about the mean of the two forces, and with relatively small numbers of participants in each. Figure 2.4 shows that happened in some of the engagements and how it was possible, from the Chinese Eye data, to create structures of these mini-battles. Some occurred simultaneously, effectively in parallel, while others involved the participants in a series of mini-battles through time. Interestingly, this division into separate small-scale battles was confirmed by war diary data from Second World War armoured engagements. Until recently the belief had been that this no longer applied in view of the post-war developments towards anti-armour weapons with much increased effective ranges. That the Second World War pattern was still relevant provided perhaps the first hint that historical data might be a useful aid to modern operational analysis.

For a simple analysis we took the mean local force ratio or 'odds' for each whole battle as being the ratio of summed attack to summed forces in all of the constituent mini battles. We found that that this ratio did correlate with casualties (Figure 2.5).

We next had to examine why we had such a variety of battles in which two similar forces met on generally similar ground and yet there were wide variations in mean local force ratios. A comparison of these ratios with the linear densities of the two forces - expressed as a density ratio - showed that for a number of scenarios local odds and density ratio were related in a simple linear manner (Fig 2.6).

THE STRESS OF BATTLE

SCENARIO 3

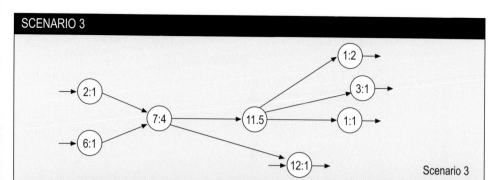

Scenario 3

SCENARIO 5

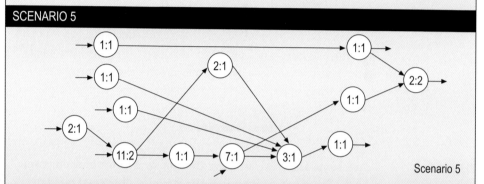

Scenario 5

SCENARIO 12

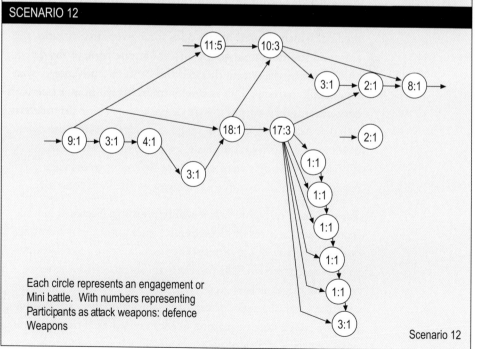

Each circle represents an engagement or
Mini battle. With numbers representing
Participants as attack weapons: defence
Weapons

Scenario 12

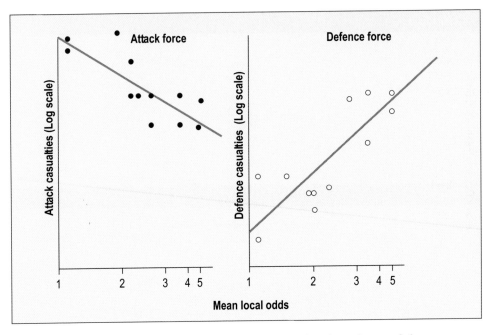

Figure 2.5
Relation between
Casualties and Mean
Local Odds

Yet, some scenarios lay above this line by a factor of about two, and others lay below by a similar factor, as illustrated by the dotted boundary lines in Fig 2.6. Considering first those above the line, which showed higher odds for a given density ratio, the common feature was an attack directed at one flank of the defence, either because the terrain dictated this or to take advantage of weak flank defences. This is simply understood - if an attack force concentrates on a part of a wide defence, then those defenders to either side who are within range, can engage, but if the defence terminates at a physical obstacle, eg a lake or wooded hills, or is divided by a ridge, then only those defenders to one side can engage. Hence the two-to-one increase in the local force ratio.

Turning back to Figure 2.4, it will be seen that Scenario No 12 incorporated a series of successive 1:1 encounters, which was at odds with many of the other scenarios. The reason for this was simply one of terrain. The attackers advanced across a series of transverse ridges as they were engaged by the defence. The battle took the form of a series of very small engagements, each involving just one attack tank or platoon as they crested each ridge. The size of the attack was thus of little advantage as it was effectively

THE STRESS OF BATTLE

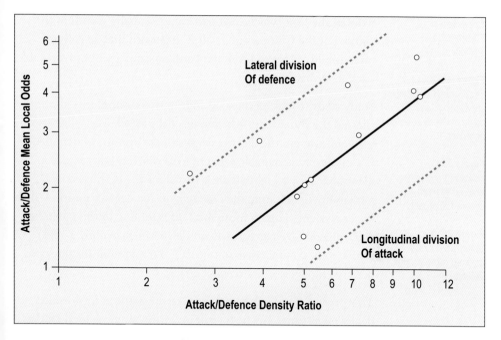

Figure 2.6
Relation between
Densities of Deployment
and Mean Local Odds

committed piecemeal in a series of low force ratio encounters. Although this battle scenario and another similar one were within a factor of one to two of the overall force ratio, there appeared to be no limiting value to this factor which could vary with the attacker's longitudinal density.

These results indicated some useful tactical lessons:

a. From lateral division of the defence the attack may benefit in odds, by attacking when the defence is handicapped by an edge effect, as along the sides of wide valleys.

b. Conversely the defence should increase the density of defence close to such edges.

c. From longitudinal division of the attack, the defence can draw considerable benefit by deploying behind transverse ridges to engage the attack in small groups - a part of the benefit of the reverse slope.

The battle structure indicated by this analysis also suggested a different interpretation of Lanchester's square law when applied to real terrain. It had been frequently assumed that intervisibility reduced the time which each participant actually spends in the battle, but the Chinese Eye analysis suggested that actually intervisibility helps to break the battle up into a series of separable Lanchester battles.

Study of the course of these armour/anti-armour battles also allowed the situation in which part of the attack force closed with and overran the defence at given odds, yet to be identified. If a minimum acceptable value of local overrun odds could be identified, say no higher than 1:1 to allow the defence a 50% probability of defeating the attackers on the defence position, then the equivalent scenario mean local odds leading to this could be determined. Given an estimate of defence density, this would enable force commanders to calculate the minimum deployment density required for a successful attack.

This process thus leads to a picture of the battle as a two-sided deployment game in which attrition in the resulting local battles determines the ability of parts of the attack to close with, overrun and compromise the defence. Total casualties in themselves do not determine battle outcome, but the attainment of local superiority does.

Other Chinese Eye lessons related to fire control. Two aspects concerned the initial opening of fire by the defence and the question of overkill. Both have tended to have been treated somewhat differently in the modelling field from what happens in the real world. When to open fire is a key aspect of the defence. Often the moment is delayed to prevent premature disclosure of the lay-out of the defence and to allow the attack to become committed and vulnerable to several defence weapons. On the other side of the coin, the defence surrenders the opportunity to engage targets at longer range, especially with ATGW, and thus improve the odds in its favour at an early stage.

Chinese Eye provided one very clear example of the way in which an attack can benefit from early defence fire (see Figure 2.7). The defence planned to hold fire until the attack was committed at close range in the open, and the attack plan - to keep away from the left hand village and the tree line on the top of the escarpment

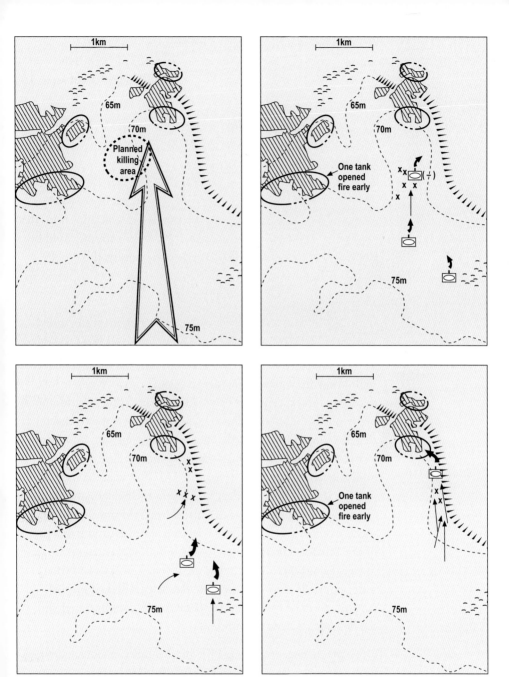

to their right - played into the hands of this plan (Figure 2.7.1).
However, one defence tank could not resist opening fire as the
closest company approached (Figure 2.7.2). While half of this

One Company of attack force on Ex CHINESE EYE (Scenario 2)

leading company were quickly knocked out, the remainder veered right, away from those defenders engaging them. When it was found that the survivors of the lead company were progressing better on this side, the following companies were also ordered in this direction (Figure 2.7.3). They were now moving turret down to two troops of the defence - hugging the tree line they had originally set out to avoid (Figure 2.7.4). This enabled them to overrun the right hand village and unpin the defence. Thus the early opening of fire by the defence allowed the attack, by three successive corrections, to find a covered approach route to a part of the defence. Likewise, there were several insistences on Chinese Eye of the attacker overrunning the defence, in spite of earlier suffering heavy casualties, because the defence lacked mutual support. In these cases, too, the defence was compromised and the defenders forced to withdraw.

Once the defence has opened fire on the attack, there are defined drills and procedures to maximise its effectiveness by avoiding unnecessary overkill. Yet, Chinese Eye revealed that overkill took place as if no effective drill was being used to prevent it. The deduction from this is that any target's probability of being hit

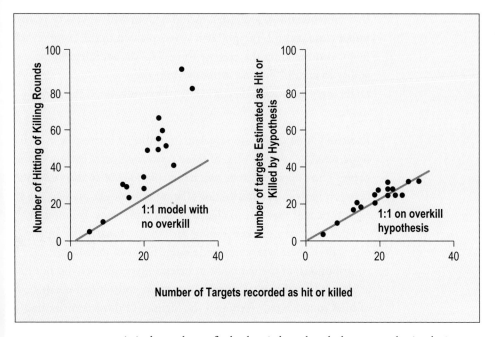

Figure 2.8
Comparison of Interactive Trials Data with Conventional Modelling Assumption and Simple Hypothesis for Overkill

is independent of whether it has already been struck. Analysis showed that the main reason for overkill was that once a force is deployed each element of it views the battle from a different perspective by virtue of its deployment position and will act accordingly, often in spite of being informed by radio of what is happening elsewhere. We will return to this aspect.

Plotting the number of rounds recorded as hits in each Chinese Eye scenario against the number of targets struck and comparing them to the hypothetical situation (the solid line in the graph above), in which there is a force ratio of 1 and there are no incidences of overkill, reveals that the more targets hit, the more the incidence of overkill. In other words, as the intensity of fire relative to target size increases so does overkill, from a factor of 1 at 20% casualties to almost 3 at 95% casualties.

The left-hand graph indicates the divergence of the simple no overkill assumption from Red Force performance, while the right hand graph shows that the simple hypothesis for overkill fits interactive trial results.

In a subsequent low level trial, including four Milan ATGW teams under close control, the problem was explained to the experienced major commanding the exercise force. He was confident in his ability to control fire and avoid overkill. Even so, despite a simple target array advancing on one route, the results fitted the above model.

Exercise Chinese Eye also revealed a number of interesting aspects of personal behaviour. One of these concerned participation in the battle. There appeared to be two main components to the variations between individual contributions, being in the right place at the right time and that due to character and experience. Examples of both were very marked among the defence force tanks. In any one action, there was a very wide range between individual contributions; of the ten tanks in defence, typically two did not fire at all, while at the other extreme two tanks contributed nearly half of total rounds fired. Although the identity of those contributing most did change from battle to battle, there was also a trend for certain individual tanks to contribute more or less than others. A partial explanation appeared to be that command tanks contributed less, since their commanders had other duties to perform than just fighting their tanks.

Another aspect was individual errors and misperceptions. When deploying the defending combat team, the commander made his own reconnaissance and gave orders to his troop leaders. On arrival in their assigned areas, these attempted to deploy in position with fields of fire as ordered, but on occasions they made detailed changes to optimise the inevitable balance between concealment and field of fire. Some of these changes affected the total mutual cover of ground by the combat team. One example occurred on the scenario in Figure 2.7, when the troop eventually overrun had two tanks set further back than ordered, reducing their coverage of the route finally discovered by the attack.

When contact had been made with the enemy, a whole set of problems could arise from late contact reports - or no reports at all. In some cases communication problems were the cause, while in others the sub-unit was too busy reacting to the situation with which it was presented. Associated with this problem of the passage of information was that of misperception of the attacker's movements. Often he would be reported going into dead ground, but the varying perspectives from the different defence positions resulted in different interpretations of the attacker's intention. This sometimes led to phantom forces being suspected and searched for, sometimes preventing redeployment of defence to meet the real threat. In sum, these were indications of the 'fog of war' which is present on any battlefield.

A miscellany of other problems affected the defence, including breaches of fire control (as in Figure 2.7), breakdowns and boggings, all becoming critical if they occurred in contact with the enemy.

The attack force had its own parallel problems, despite using simple tactics. Differences in perception of the defence became critical for a dispersed moving force which was also having problems with locating its own positions. Co-ordination of the separate companies was also difficult as they moved around features or were delayed by minor obstacles.

Exercise Kings Ride

Fundamentally, Chinese Eye had, through the ability to stage realistic interactive field trials, thanks to Simfire, revealed many insights into the mechanisms of the armour/anti-armour battle. However, to obtain a more comprehensive picture, the same methodology needed to be applied to infantry combat.

By 1978 Simgun, an infantry version of Simfire, had been developed. This enabled a further series of interactive field trials to be set up under Exercise Kings Ride. The initial set comprised fifty infantry platoon attacks against a section and took place on a training area in England. At the same time, there were calibration tests on the equipment.

The next phase was to introduce an all arms aspect. This was based on attacks by one tank company or one tank company and one mechanised infantry company using Warsaw Pact tactics

Solartron prototype 'SIMGUN' fitted to SLR for use on KINGS RIDE trials. The control Box and the two detectors (to be shoulder mounted) are also shown

against a company group comprising two infantry platoons, one tank troop and an ATGW detachment. To differentiate between the engagement of men and tanks, separate pulsed laser frequencies were used for each and the various forms of fire were presented as shown opposite in Figure 2.9.

As with Chinese Eye, pyrotechnics were used to represent weapon signatures and representative infantry weapons were made to look as much as possible like the genuine article, including being of approximately the same weight.

This next phase of Kings Ride was carried out on terrain in Germany similar to that used in Chinese Eye. Sixteen scenarios were replicated in terms of forces, deployments and terrain and a further twenty-five each took place on different pieces of ground. Further sets considered woods and attacks on entrenched positions with obstacles. In some cases, dismounted infantry were studied. These trials served to confirm the armour/anti-armour trials findings, especially in terms of overkill, as the Figure 2.10 opposite demonstrates:

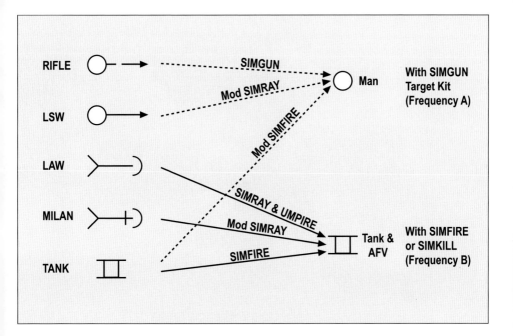

Figure 2.9
Schematic of Trials
representation of
Anti-Personnel and
Anti-Armour Fire

Figure 2.10
Comparison of
Interactive Trials Data
With Conventional
modelling Assumption
and Simple Hypothesis
for Overkill

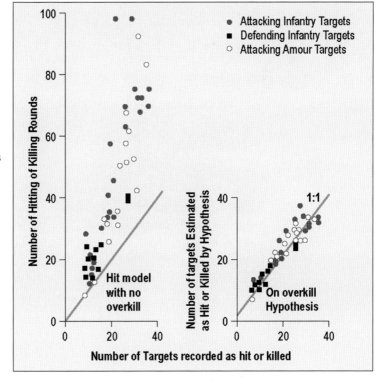

THE STRESS OF BATTLE

This confirmed that it was possible to predict the number of casualties in an attack force through the number of killing hits achieved by the defence, although this only became significant at levels of 25-30% casualties inflicted. However, as stated above, at the 95% level overkill increased by a factor of three over the 1:1 force ratio with no overkill hypothesis. In the interactive combat trials the participation rate by those with targets in view (and permission to fire) was 90%. However there were then aspects of degradation compared to the simpler one-sided assessments of performance, as witnessed on the firing range. Rates of fire by defence weapons was degraded to 14% of the one-sided situation for rifles and to approximately 60% of that for machine guns. In addition, defence fire against moving targets indicated hit probabilities of approximately 40% of those against static targets.

Taking capability on a practice range as a base line, the broad factors by which the casualties inflicted by defence small arms fire against an attack force would be reduced are as summarised overleaf:

Cause of difference	Factor
Non-participation	90%
Rate of fire	40%
Target Movement	14% (rifle), 60% (mg)
Overall factor (before overkill)	5 % (rifle), 21% (mg)

The Chinese Eye and Kings Ride trials had produced some very revealing pointers as to what happens in combat, especially in terms of combat degradation. The ability to produce interactive scenarios, thanks to Simfire, had added a fresh dimension to field trials, and that was apart from its value as a training aid. But field trials could not recreate the stresses of real combat and the findings this far could only be regarded as speculative.

One significant indication of this was when the defensive fire performance on Kings Ride was compared with results obtained from firings on a range under test conditions. It revealed that rifle performance was degraded by a factor of 20 and machine guns by a factor of five. Much of this could be explained by differences between the two environments. Factors such as target movement, and the reduced rate of fire brought about by the difficulties in target detection in a tactical situation, as well as overkill, contributed. There was also the question of individual performance. Inevitably, some men had more opportunities to fire than others during the field trials and there were differences in individual skills.

It was likely that there would be further weapons degradation and reduction in individual performance under live fire. That this was probably so was borne out by the 1982 Falklands campaign. Infantry behaviour was remarkably different from that exhibited in the Kings Ride simulated battles. In particular, it was noted that during attacks in the Falklands the infantry overran the defences, while in the Kings Ride scenarios they were usually stopped in front of the defensive position.

Simultaneously, in 1982 the Director General of Army Training suggested that the possibilities of including morale and stress

Troops of 1 Para Regt and Chieftain tank of Queens Royal Irish Hussars (showing SIMFIRE destruction pyrotechnics) on Ex KINGS RIDE IV (Salisbury Plain)

in battle in operational analysis assessments. The result was a symposium organised by the Director of the Scientific Advisory Group (Army). While this did not reveal any new insights, it did provide the stimulus for further investigation. There was also a request from the war games department at RARDE's Fort Halstead establishment to apply live fire conditions to the Kings Ride field trials.

Analyses of Chinese Eye and Kings Ride had confirmed that human factors had much influence on weapons effectiveness, something which had not really been taken into account in modelling and field exercises. It was now a question of working out how to quantify this influence. The answer would be Historical Analysis.

CHAPTER THREE
The Beginning of Historical Analysis

Only study of the past can give us a sense of reality and show us how the soldier will fight in the future.

Ardant du Picq* *Battle Studies* first published in France in 1880

The Chinese Eye and King's Ride studies had identified that combat degradation was caused in part by an inability to acquire targets and a lack of fire discipline, which resulted in overkill. There are, however, clearly other less definable other influences at work on the battlefield and these are largely bound up in morale. The degree present has a direct bearing on the soldier's ability to overcome the natural fear of combat, especially when facing incoming fire, and to withstand shock and surprise.

On the surface, morale *per se* is very difficult to quantify and, indeed, little attempt has been made in the past to do so. In September 1945, the British Army's Deputy Scientific Adviser, Brigadier Nigel Balchin, later the author of several successful novels, including *The Small Back Room* set in a World War 2 OR section, was asked by the Director of Tactical Investigation to comment on a possible study on the subject. He replied:

> "I have been trying for five years to get something done about a scientific study of morale and am naturally delighted at this high level recognition of the need for it. At the same time, however, certain difficulties always arise in a study of this kind, and I hope you will forgive me if I am completely frank about them.
>
> Morale is a subject on which everybody in the Army has opinions and practically nobody has reliable information. Indeed, the *need* for information is seldom recognised. The soldier will readily admit that there are other people who know more than he

---

* Colonel Ardant du Picq was a French army officer and veteran of the Crimean War and campaigns in Syria and Algeria. He fell at the head of his regiment in August 1870, in the opening weeks of the Franco-Prussian War. His writings, published posthumously, had much influence on the French Army, especially the belief that élan was its most positive characteristic and that this was best utilised in the attack.

does about ballistics or fragmentation. But he is much less ready to admit that anyone else knows more about men. The understanding of man, he feels, is his profession.

It is a fact that scattered through the Army there is a great deal of experience and knowledge of the problems of morale. But it has never been collected or systematised. Everybody's opinion depends on his own experience and observation, which may or may not be representative.

The result is that any discussion of morale divides sharply into two stages:

1. The stage of woolly abstractions in which people talk solemnly of "leadership" or "discipline" or "group spirit" without ever defining the meaning of these phrases in practice;

   And

2. The all-too-concrete stage, in which the whole subject suddenly degenerates into discussions about supplies of beer.

   I suggest that what is missing is the step between these two which will connect the big abstractions with the small concrete details. We all know that one of the main requirements for good morale is good leadership. But "good leadership" means *doing* and *being* something. What, in concrete and practical terms, does it mean doing and being?

   I suggest therefore that no report by a high level committee on this matter is the slightest use unless the high level committee has at its disposal some agency to obtain for it a mass of factual data and the sociological and psychological interpretation of this data. The army never employs any of the people whose job it is to study the problems of groups of human beings. Until it decides to do so, it can only go on guessing and using nice big phrases which mean nothing whatever. For my own part, to be frank, I am sick of talking about morale. What I want now is to see the Army collect some facts about it.[1]"

He amplified his thoughts in a paper written a month later, pointing out:

> "It is only during the last four years of this war that any serious attempt has been made to take the study of morale out of the field of platitudes and undefined phrases, and to make a factual analysis of its mechanism and the principles underlying it. Even so, the effort has been scrappy, uncoordinated, and on a very small scale."

And:

> "It is difficult for anyone who has been associated with the work to derive much satisfaction from the progress made during the war with the study of battle morale. Considering the overwhelming importance of the subject, the effort made has been pathetically small and slow. Even as late as 1943, the best observations on the morale effect of bombardment were still those produced at Valenciennes in 1918.* The moral may be to the physical as three is to one, but the fact remains that at a time when literally hundreds of scientists were engaged in studying fragmentation and muzzle velocities, there was not a single man engaged full time in the study of those morale effects which are all that 95% of shells, bombs and bullets produce.

> The soldier must accept some share of the blame for this situation. He has paid lip-service to the importance of morale ...

> In the writer's view, however, the scientist and technician have been far more to blame. Morale is an extremely difficult subject, and to the scientist who likes above everything to deal in measurable facts, its frequent absence of "concreteness" has often made it very uncomfortable one. There has been a widespread tendency amongst scientists to feel that this was one of the subjects on which it was safer to be a critic than to risk one's reputation for "soundness" by putting forward any constructive suggestion.

---

* Balchin is presumably referring to the attack by the Canadian Corps against strong defences at Valenciennes on 1 November 1918. The whole of the Corps heavy and field artillery was involved and the Germans were forced to withdraw after 24 hours fighting.

If the individual scientist's reputation for infallibility is considered important, this is reasonable. But the fact is that on many of these issues (such as the design of bombardments) the soldier constantly had to make *some* decision. The alternatives are to base this decision on pure guesswork, or on a view which, while it cannot be proved for lack of data, is at least derived from careful study and supported by such facts as are available. The scientist's attitude has too often been that he preferred to give no advice (and thus to escape responsibility) rather than to give the best results he could, making it quite clear that such advice was tentative.[2]"

Balchin's views are worth reproducing in detail, since they explain very clearly the problems that existed in trying to get to grips with a subject which, on the surface, is largely an abstract one. There had, however, been a wartime report which did provide suggestions over how battlefield morale could be measured. The author was Lt Col Lionel Wigram, a keen Territorial who was the commandant the first Battle School, which was set up by GHQ Home Forces to improve combat training in the aftermath of the disastrous 1940 campaign in France. In July 1943 he went to Sicily to follow the campaign as an observer of the behaviour of infantrymen in battle. His principle finding was that in every platoon there were 'six gutful men who will go anywhere', with 'twelve "sheep" who will follow a short distance behind if they are well led". But there were also 'four to six who will run away'. It made uncomfortable reading, and apparently General Montgomery suppressed it on the grounds that it would be bad for morale. In addition, Wigram himself lost his temporary rank and was posted to a battalion in Italy as a Major, only to be killed.[3]

Wigram's report was an honest attempt to provide a realistic and dispassionate picture of precisely what happened on the battlefield. His findings on combat participation were supported to a significant degree by a post-war American study. Lt Col (later Brig Gen) S L A Marshall was commissioned by the US Army immediately after the end of World War 2 to provide combat history. He used post-action interviews for his principal sources.

Not content with merely accumulating facts, Marshall sought to elicit general truths of what happened in combat by the analysis of a large number of particular examples. From an extensive set of battles in the Pacific and North-West Europe he derived some generalised concepts, as well as preparing detailed histories. The gist of his findings was that on average only 15 men in 100 would take any active part with their weapons, and seldom above 25% even under intense local pressure. Men with heavier weapons showed a higher participation than this 15% mean, and riflemen tended to be lower. His findings were accepted by the US Army and attempts made to improve the situation. He also published them in a book, *Men Against Fire*.[4] In the Korean War, Marshall claimed, albeit with qualifications, an increase in participation rate by US soldiers:

> "When the ground and conditions permit it the measure of willing participation is more than double the World War II averages ..... The chronic non-firer is an exception under the conditions of the Korean war."[5]

Subsequent commentators have pointed out, however, that Marshall employed no 'statistical formulation or scholarly research' and merely used his own experience and subjective observations. Yet, he appeared to have stumbled across 'a profound truth'.[6, 7]

Marshall proposed a variety of possible reasons for non-participation. These varied from fear to dislike of killing. He suggested that the difference in behaviour between riflemen and heavy weapon crews could be due to a subjective assessment of the pay-off of participation - "*will the possible effect on attack casualties of my active participation be worth the possible adverse effect on me*" or, "*is it worth it?*" However, there are a number of other possible reasons for this difference with multi-crewed weapons. It could simply be because at least one member of the crew will be active, or because more senior and experienced men are assigned to the more important weapons. Another consideration is the cohesion and mutual support generated amongst members of small closely-knit teams.

The effectiveness of Defence Rifle Fire

Both Marshall and Wigram, although we were not aware of the latter's contribution at the time, seemed to indicate a method by which we could extrapolate our field trials work to actual combat situations. But no one had actually carried out any studies to confirm Marshall's findings. We therefore needed to carry out our own historical analysis. It began with a study of actions during the Boer War (1899-1902) because the author happened to be reading a book about it at the time. Despite the seemingly bloody battles of the early months of the conflict and the resolute Boer defence, the attack casualties per defence rifleman were much lower than might have been expected from our field trials.

But, given the nature of recorded combat data, the comparison with the field trials could only be at a level of aggregation, that is, an overall total of attack casualties in an attempted assault, without knowing at what stage they occurred or their cause, compared with the quantity of defence weapons or men. Furthermore, defence casualties often covered merely killed and captured, and neglecting, in terms of combat participation, those who withdrew or escaped.

In comparing these figures, we were also faced with the possible variations of degradation between weapons in line with the Marshall finding of greater non-participation by riflemen than by heavy weapon crews. We could not ignore this possible difference, nor could we overlook the effects of defence or attack indirect fire.

The diagram below shows weapon usage through time and indicates the way into the problem. It may be seen that in the 1860s rifles replaced muskets, and were for the next 50 years the main small arm in use. Although machine guns were used in the Boer War and earlier, it was not until the First World War that they became a major weapon. At about the same time, artillery fire changed from direct to observed indirect fire, and tanks came into use as a means of reducing the defence's direct fire advantage. Anti-tank guns, other than simple expedients, date from the Second World War.

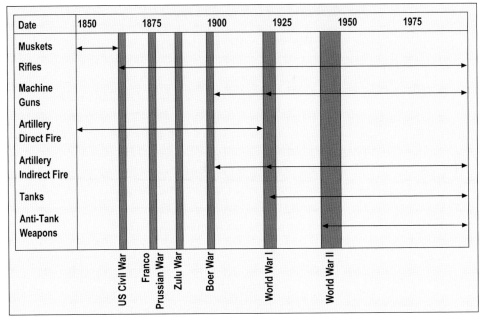

Figure 3.1
Weapons in use in specific conflicts

Since, besides rifles, only direct artillery fire was significant prior to 1914, we decided to extend the initial investigation of the Boer War to include other campaigns in this era to obtain an estimate of rifle effectiveness. This was especially since there was a very wide scatter in the Boer War results. However, the field trials had demonstrated the sensitivity of firing rates to the number of available targets, while the use of force ratios had allowed much of the scatter to be explained.

We applied this approach to the earlier US Civil War of 1861-65, for which there was considerably more data for mainly rifle defence. An examination of that collected from published sources gave another set of results for analysis and these showed the same order of results and a similar effect with force ratio as for the Boer War. Furthermore, neither set of battles showed marked difference in successful and unsuccessful attack casualties. This can be explained if one assumes that the extra attack casualties incurred in continuing to close with the defence are roughly balanced by those suffered while going to ground and withdrawing.

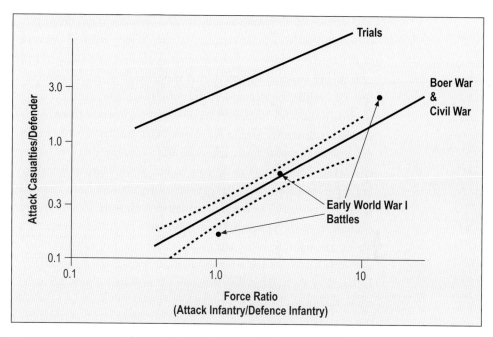

Figure 3.2
Comparison of rifle casualty estimates from trials data, Boer War & Civil War (pooled) and World War I

These findings allowed the data extracted from these two wars to be pooled and used for a combined analysis. Results are shown in Figure 3.2. As with field trials results, these were plotted as attack casualties per defender against force ratio so as to provide a measure of target availability. Logarithmic scales were used since they allow for a wide range of values to be represented. The results are shown as a best fit regression line, and with 95 per cent confidence limits for casualties as a measure of the spread of data.

Other battles were also examined for evidence of any differences from the trend. The 1870 Franco-Prussian War showed similar and lower casualties, while the epic defence of Rorke's Drift, in the aftermath of the disaster at Isandhlwana during the 1879 Zulu War, appeared consistent with the trend. Also plotted on the graph were three early actions in the First World War with British rifle defence and a few machine guns present. These were the battle of Mons, the defence of Landrecies by 4 (Guards) Brigade on 25 August 1914, and the Indian Dehra Dun Brigade at Neuve Chapelle on 27 October 1914 and they also followed the trend. None showed more effective use of rifles than in the field trials.

The sample of 47 battles in which rifles were the main defensive weapon provided a good estimate of their effect, with 65 per cent of the variation explained by force ratio, and the remaining 35 per cent giving a spread similar to that expected from comparison between similar battles under trial conditions. However, the order of effectiveness for rifles in defence was very different from the combat trials results. Figure 3.2 shows these simulated battle results, reduced to the same form and scale and assuming that our highest trial level of combat, with up to a company visible to a defender, is a representative slice of the generally larger battles from historical data. The similarity in trend of casualties with force ratio is at once evident from the gradients, but with battle casualties/riflemen about one tenth of those attributable on trials, possibly down to one eighth at 3:1 force ratio. In absolute value, attack casualties inflicted by each defending riflemen present were about 0.5 at 3:1 ratio, falling to the 0.25 at unity force ratio.

This 10:1 ratio between the trials' results and the results of the wars studied is consistent with Marshall's participation factor of at most 15 per cent for rifle degradation (which implies a degradation factor of at least 7:1). The trials' results and wars studied also have similar slopes. Marshall's findings could explain the difference in kill ratio for rifles, but what about heavy weapons which Marshall found less degraded?

The effectiveness of Defence Machine Gun Fire

In general, defensive forces with machine guns also deployed mortars. In order to make any examination of these heavy weapons, it was therefore necessary to separate the effectiveness of machine guns in causing casualties from that of mortars.

A Second World War study by a British OR team had examined casualties on the D-Day beaches in relation to a detailed survey of defence weapons present and used.[8] This resulted in remarkably consistent figures for total casualties per machine gun and mortar present and fired, with a relative effectiveness of three machine guns being equal to one 81-mm mortar in casualty effect. This provided the basis for a link between direct and indirect defence

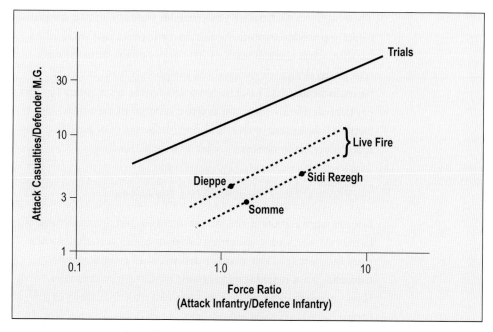

Figure 3.3
Comparison of MG
casualty estimates from
trials and combat data.

fire effect. Other defending indirect fire weapons were calculated as "equivalent machine guns" by scaling the ratio of their sustained rate of fire and area of effectiveness to those of the 81-mm mortar. With this defence indirect fire relationship and the estimated effectiveness of defence rifle fire, it was now possible to use attack casualty data, deduct casualties attributable to defence rifles and then apportion those remaining between "equivalent machine guns".

Three sets of battles were found to allow this examination of machine gun effectiveness. These included the first day of the Somme Offensive on 1 July 1916, averaging data from over one hundred battalion attacks on an 18 mile frontage, with the assumption for the time being that the preparatory bombardment had little effect. Battles from the Second World War were also selected in which neither preparatory artillery bombardment nor attack tanks were significant. The Canadian attack on Blue Beach during the August 1942 Dieppe Raid, in which the attacking battalion suffered massive casualties, was one such action. Four individual battalion defences by New Zealand troops in the Sidi Rezegh battles during Operation Crusader in Libya in November 1941 also provided data.

These were compared with trials' data in Figure 3.3; they are related to the unity force ratio using the gradient previously established for rifles from combat analysis (the slopes of the broken lines), which was similar to the gradient established from trials. The figure indicates that machine guns in combat were about 15-25 per cent as effective as on interactive combat trials, a degradation factor of about one in five, and notably better than for rifles; this again is generally consistent with Marshall's findings.

The Effects of Attack Suppressive Fire: Bombardment

Further examination of the First World War and Second World War battles showed many with even lower machine gun effectiveness than this, a few so low that the deduction of estimated rifle casualties left a negative estimate for machine gun casualties. It was possible to associate some of these with the effects of preparatory artillery bombardment. Again some Second World War operational research studies (unpublished) had examined sets of battles, including estimates of artillery bombardment duration (from fire plans) and density from crater count. In each set, the attack casualties had been related to density of bombardment, and the studies showed an effect of reducing attack casualties with increasing density of bombardment. However, due to the special conditions of each set of battles, these bore little relation (in terms of attack casualties per defender) to each other, even when extrapolated to zero bombardment.

In order to use the results from this data we had to make use of two properties of the straight line graph - the intercept and its slope. We began with a simple example, the D-Day beaches, plotting casualties per defending machine gun (vertically) against the density of the attack artillery bombardment (horizontally) (Figure 3.4). This provided us both with an estimate of effectiveness at zero artillery (the intercept with the vertical axis), and the degradation with bombardment (the slope of the line). A note on the layout of these graphs may be helpful here; again the vertical axis is logarithmic for the same reason as before, but the horizontal

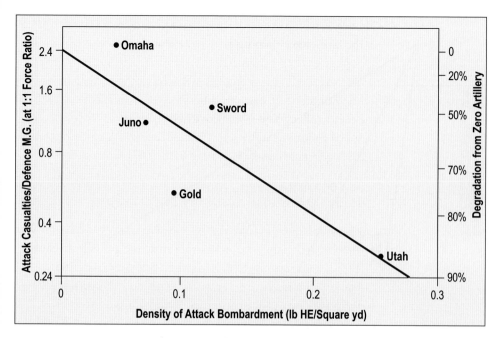

Figure 3.4
Effect of density of preparatory attack bombardment on attack casualties/defender, hence defence degradation

axis is linear in scale to allow the expected form of relationship (a negative exponential) to be represented as a straight line.

As a means of comparing the set of battles in Figure 3.4 with other sets, we can consider effectiveness relative to that at zero artillery bombardment. If we scale results from different sets of battles relative to their intercept, and compare their fractional degradation (right hand scale of Figure 3.4) due to bombardment density, we can study relative effects of other bombardment characteristics, such as duration. In order to compare the effectiveness of bombardment duration in these different sets of battles, Figure 3.5 brings the three sets of data together by comparing their fractional degradation from zero bombardment, as explained above. It is worth noting here the three sets of battles involved:

- Groups of beaches in the June 1944 D-Day landings in Operation Overlord, taken as the five main beaches. (From Figure 3.4).

- Four battalion attacks on the opening day of Operation Clipper, 18 November 1944, the British XXX Corps pinching out of the Geilenkirchen salient on the German border, and

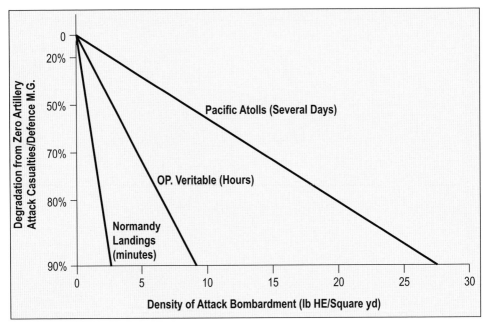

Figure 3.5
Effect of duration
of bombardment
on the degradation
in infantry firepower
for a given density
of bombardment

twelve battalion attacks on 8 February 1945, the first day of Operation Veritable, First Canadian Army's offensive to clear from the south-east of Nijmegen to the Lower Rhine. The data was drawn from OR reports made shortly after the events.[9]

• US landings on the Central Pacific Islands of Makin, Engebi, Eniwetok, Parry Roi, Namur, Kwajalein, and Ebeye, the data being drawn from a 1945 AORG Memorandum.[10]

Air bombardment was included in total bombardment density.

Each set was characterised by a different duration of bombardment - several minutes for D-Day, several hours for Operations Veritable and Clipper, and days for the Pacific Island assaults. Bearing in mind their relative durations, the relative slopes of these lines form a consistent pattern - for a given total weight of bombardment the shortest/sharpest, that for the Normandy landings, provides the greatest degradation for a given weight of bombardment, and the bombardment was the shortest of the three in duration.

The relationship of these sets of battles can be approximated by the graphical relationship shown in Figure 3.6, effectively a series

THE STRESS OF BATTLE

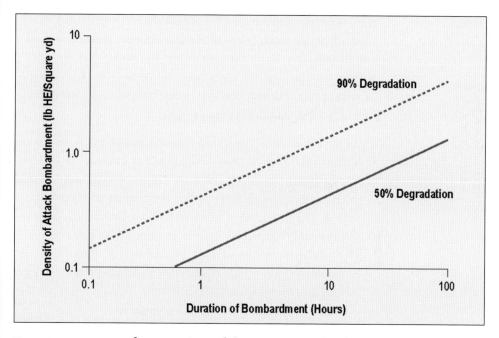

Figure 3.6
Relationship between density of preparatory attack bombardment and its duration to achieve a given level of degradation in infantry firepower, from zero artillery density.

of cross sections of the previous graph. This plots density of bombardment, vertically, against duration, horizontally. On these axes a series of lines of constant degradation can be drawn; at 90 per cent degradation a density of 0.4 lb high explosive (HE) per square yard over a duration of one hour is as effective as a density of 4 lb HE per square yard in 100 hours. In each case 90 per cent further degradation on the zero bombardment case is achieved, that is, by a further factor of ten, on the effectiveness in Figures 3.4 and 3.5.

From these curves a relationship for degradation due to artillery can be devised in terms of density and duration. Thus, the results of these and other individual battles can be corrected to zero artillery bombardment, increasing the actual casualties to a notional figure to be expected had there been no preparatory bombardment.

The Effects of Attack Suppressive Fire: Tanks

Even after applying this correction there remained several battles in which defence weapon effectiveness was substantially lower than the figures I have quoted. Two examples help to point out the reasons for the differences. The unpublished Second World War Operational Research Study of the casualties per defence weapon and the effects of bombardment on the D-Day beaches was left with an unexplained difference between the two US beaches and between US and British beaches. It did, however, note the effects of attack armour in the comment:

'In the British Areas particularly on Juno and Sword, Amphibious Sherman (DD) tanks proved of the greatest assistance to infantry in overcoming the beach defences. This experience was repeated at Utah where the DDs supported the infantry with marked success. The comparative failure of DDs on Omaha was probably due primarily to the bad weather and not to any unsuitability. From the point of view of firepower and tactical employment ... experience on Juno showed that they could exert a decisive influence on fighting on the beach.'[11]

Another example, albeit the extreme, is the low defence effectiveness in Operations Clipper and Veritable, with less than one tenth the attacking casualty/ defence machine gun estimated above, even when corrected to zero artillery bombardment. A feature of these operations was the massive AFV support available, with the five infantry divisions supported by over 800 AFVs from army tank brigades and the specialised armour of the 79th Armoured Division.

Qualitative comments on the effectiveness of attack AFVs in suppressing defence small arms fire are not rare, however, and although this was the original *raison d'être* of the tank in the First World War and great effort and ingenuity were expended to get them ashore on D-Day, there has apparently been no attempt at quantitatively assessing their effect in the role of infantry suppression. Collecting together the available casualty data, deducting casualties due to rifles and correcting for defence indirect fire and attack preparatory bombardment, I attempted an examination against a measure of tank density. In order to bring together different size battles, the tank density was represented as a type of force ratio - attack tanks per defence machine gun. Furthermore, for each tank added there is a progressively smaller additional effect and so this ratio was plotted, as with artillery

Figure 3.7
Defence MG,
effectiveness and
attack tank density
for World War II battles
excluding D-Day
Beaches. (At 1:1 Force
Ratio. Zero Artillery
Bombardment)

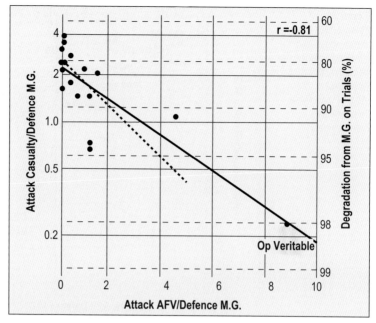

bombardment, to a logarithmic vertical scale and linear horizontal scale, allowing the likely relationship to be plotted as a straight line.

The Second World War battles do show a significant effect when plotted in this way. Two sets of results were taken separately. All of the Second World War for which data was available, except the D-Day beaches, are shown in Figure 3.7. While the points do at first sight appear scattered, the correlation coefficient of 0.8 is fairly high, indicating 65 per cent of the variation is explained by the relationship. Moreover, the best-fit line through the points is robust to the inclusion of the extreme point (for Operation Veritable). This might be thought to have been driving it, but the broken line representing the relationship if Operation Veritable is excluded shows this is not so.

Note that, at the zero attack tanks, effectiveness was 2.2 casualties/weapon, or 18 per cent that of machine gun trials, a degradation factor of six, consistent with the earlier estimates for machine guns in Figure 3.3. When the attack AFV/defence MG ratio rises to 8, the MG effectiveness is reduced by a further factor of ten.

Figure 3.8
Defence MG
effectiveness and
attack tank density for
Normandy beaches,
World War II.
(At 1:1 Force Ratio,
Zero Artillery
Bombardment)

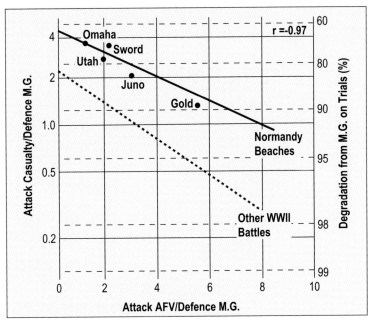

Figure 3.8 shows the D-Day beaches separately since they represented a distinct set in that they involved amphibious landing against prepared defences. As there were only five points here and since they had already been used to estimate one of the artillery curves, the best relationship for AFV/machine gun ratio was checked by successive iterations. The resultant curve had a correlation coefficient of 0.97, with the artillery curve previously estimated being subjected to only a trivial correction. This accounts for the unexplained comment in the Second World War OR analysis over the assistance provided by the armour on the British beaches and justifies its use on D-Day. The broken curve representing the other World War 2 cases involving AFVs displays a remarkably similar gradient. This provides a robust confirmation of the relationship between the two sets, although that for the D-Day beaches indicates higher casualties for zero attack tanks by a factor of approximately two. We will come to the reason for this, which is related to obstacles and fortification, shortly.

There was, however, another discrepancy. While these results confirmed the overall effectiveness of AFVs in defence suppression, below about two attack tanks per defence machine gun, the AFV

THE STRESS OF BATTLE

does not in itself make much of an impact. In contrast, consider the effective suppression of a sector of Australian defences at Tobruk on 1 May 1941. The Australian Official History recounted the attack on each half platoon post by two German tanks. These bombarded the posts, then a few infantry dismounted under cover of tank fire and dropped grenades into the weapon pits, forcing the defenders to surrender. Here effective suppression was achieved with two tanks per machine gun, and it was suppression of resolute defenders as earlier battles, especially during the Tobruk siege, had shown. The Australian problem was lack of anti-tank guns, so how would the presence of defence anti-tank fire affect attacking tanks? Simple imagination and a little further historical investigation suggested the answer - defensive anti-tank fire dilutes the attacking tanks' attention to defence small arms, since a significant part of this is given to detecting and engaging the immediate threat to the tanks themselves.

To answer this question, it was necessary to examine actions in which anti-tank guns were either not present or in insufficient numbers to have much influence. We therefore decided to look at First World War tank actions, in which the Germans had a few anti-tank rifles and had to rely largely on conventional field artillery to combat the tank. The cases studied included the major battles, such as Cambrai in November 1917 and Amiens in August 1918, in which the use of tanks was initially remarkably successful, and smaller local actions for which data was available. When plotted in the same way as before we obtain a similar curve, as shown in Figure 3.9 overleaf. Yet, there is a marked defence degradation (by a factor of ten) at about two tanks per machine gun, as noted incidentally for the 1 May 1941 attack at Tobruk, instead of the eight tanks per machine gun indicated by most Second World War battles. This means that the tanks in the First World War caused a generally greater degradation, for a given number, than tanks in the Second World War.

Pursuing the hypothesis that the presence of defence anti-tank guns diverts the attention of attack tanks from machine guns, a suggested way forward was to combine the two sets of data – the presence and non-presence of anti-tank guns - and to measure the

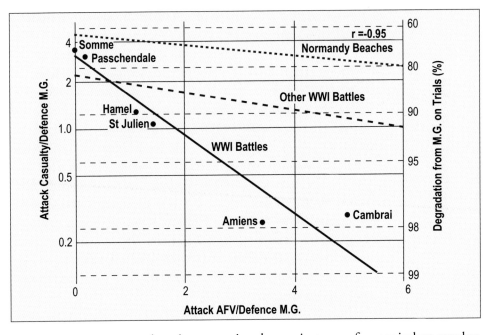

Figure 3.9
Defence MG
effectiveness and
attack tank density for
World War I battles.
(At 1:1 Force Ratio,
Zero Artillery
Bombardment)

attention given to anti-tank guns in terms of an equivalent number of defence machine guns. This figure, which we will call 'x', would be expected to reflect bigger or more powerful guns, since these present a greater threat to the tank. As a first step, we considered "typical" Second World War anti-tank guns, since attempting to differentiate between guns of different types in varying mixes would strain the limits of available data. A value of x was estimated from the extreme of the Second World War battles - Operations Veritable and Clipper. The simple attack AFV per defence MG in Figure 3.7 was 8.8, to bring this to the (simple) line of Figure 3.9 with no defence anti-tank weapons required a value of 2.2. Hence in Op Veritable the effect of defence anti-tank weapons in diluting attack fire was the equivalent of quadrupling the number of defence machine guns. This extra effective number of equivalent machine guns divided by the anti-tank weapons present gave an estimate of 15 for the factor 'x'. The value obtained was now used in all those battles with anti-tank weapons to calculate a total of equivalent defence machine guns, including the attention due to representative machine guns.

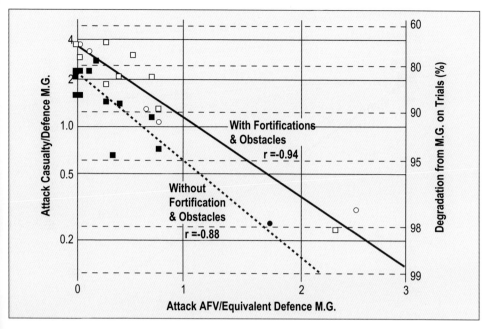

Figure 3.10
Defence MG
effectiveness and tank
density, taking account
of defence anti-tank
weapons as equivalent
MG. (At 1:1 Force
Ratio. Zero Artillery
Bombardment)

The First and Second World War sets were then plotted together
as tanks per equivalent defence machine guns, with anti-tank
weapons included in the equivalence. The First World War points
are indicated by circles showing that results from the two wars are
consistent after the correction based on one Second World War
set of battles.

The Effect of Defence Fortifications and Obstacles

This exercise revealed a further factor – the influence of prepared
defences, including obstacles. This helped to explain some of the
scatter in the earlier results and by dividing the battles in which
the defender was fighting from prepared positions from those in
which these were not present, two near parallel lines were obtained.
From this it was possible to calculate that the presence of
'fortifications' increased defence effectiveness by a factor of 1.65.

All results were now corrected to the zero fortification case, using
this 1.65 factor, and plotted as shown in Figure 3.11:

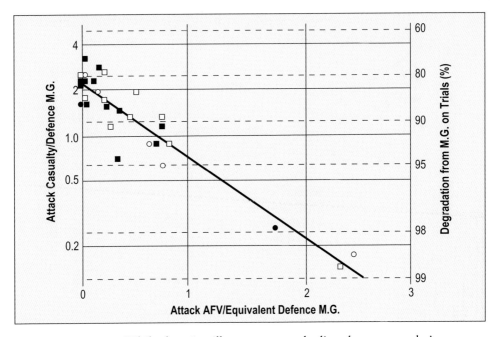

Figure 3.11
Defence MG
effectiveness and
tank density, corrected
to zero fortification.
(At 1:1 Force Ratio.
Zero Artillery
Bombardment)

While there is still some scatter, the line shows a correlation coefficient of 0.94, which means that nearly 90 per cent of the variation between battles is explained by the factors we have isolated. The remaining variation is equivalent to that between battles on our interactive trials, indicating that we could reduce it little further. The intercept of Figure 3.11 at zero AFV and zero fortification indicates two casualties per machine gun at 1:1 force ratio, close to that derived in the preliminary analysis in Figure 3.3, and indicating a degradation by a factor of six on tactical trials. Thus, the militarily believed value of AFVs in the attack is confirmed by three independent sets of results, which can themselves be related by taking account of defence anti-tank weapons and obstacles.

In comparing the effects estimated for real battles it may be noted that the mean effect of the increased tank density on the three British beaches in Normandy (Figure 3.8) in comparison with that on the two US beaches was a factor of approx 35% increased infantry casualties on the US beaches over those suffered by the British and Canadians. A later comparison (not shown here) of the use of light armour (CVR(T)) on the Falklands in support of 2 Para during the battle of Wireless Ridge indicates that here

THE STRESS OF BATTLE

(in the absence of effective defence anti-tank fire) the suppression effect caused a 75% reduction in attack infantry casualties.

Summary of the Effects Estimated

The suppressive effect of tanks on infantry in defence could now be represented in combat simulation, as can the effect of defence anti-tank weapons in attack infantry casualties. Simple examples of the effects of attack tanks and defence anti-tank weapons on a 3:1 infantry battle are shown diagrammatically in Figure 3.12.

Diagrammatic Representation of Battle		Description of Battle	Casualties to Attacking Infantry Men (Killed + Wounded)
Infantry Defence, No Anti Tank Capability (Section + M.G.)	Infantry Platoon Attack	Pure Infantry Attack at 3:1 Force Ratio	12
	Infantry Platoon Attack Supported by One Tank	Infantry Heavy Attack at 3:1 Inf. Force Ratio on Pure Infantry Defence	4
	Infantry Platoon Attack Supported by Tank Troop	Square Inf./Arm. Attack at 3:1 Inf Force Ratio on Infantry & Anti Tank Defence	0-1
Infantry Defence, Strong Anti Tank Capability (Section + M.G. + A.T. Gun)	Infantry Platoon Attack Supported by Tank Troop	Square Inf./Arm. Attack at 3:1 Inf Force Ratio on Infantry & Anti Tank Defence	10
	Infantry Platoon and Three Tank Troops Attack	Armour Heavy Attack at 3:1 Inf. Force Ratio on Infantry & Anti Tank Defence	6
	Infantry Platoon and Tank Squadron	Armour Heavy Attack at 3:1 Inf. Force Ratio on Infantry & Anti Tank Defence	4

Figure 3.12
Simple comparison of effects of attack AFV support on attack casualties in battle.

This diagram represents a "slice" through a larger battle, reflecting the finding from field trials that it can be broken down into a series of small-scale actions, and portrays a typical section defence to platoon attacks supported by a varying number of tanks. The right hand column tabulates the total attack casualties (killed and wounded) to be expected in the battle. Indirect fire effects are not shown on the diagram for simplicity, but it is possible to estimate how defence indirect fire would increase those casualties by one factor and preparatory attack bombardment would reduce them by another factor.

We realised, however, that other causes implicitly included in the above analysis could possibly further modify these degradation factors. They included leadership, training, and environmental effects and were to be pursued at a later date. We also recognised that these results were generally limited to infantry in relatively open country and that the effects in urban areas and woods might be different.

In conclusion, every battle was studied for which appropriate data could be found. The sample eventually comprised 100 actions, 47 of these related to rifle fire only and covering the period between 1860 and 1914. A further 28 battles in three sets were used to examine artillery effects and another 29 in three groups to examine AFV, anti-tank and fortifications. The robustness of the three sets was demonstrated by their similarities and they, together with the artillery set, enabled the final estimates for machine guns to be made.

Establishing a degradation factor between tactical trials and live fire resulted in two being identified, one covering rifles and the other machine guns. In addition, suppression effects due to the artillery, AFVs, and, separately, obstacle effects were assessed. Furthermore, both trials and live fire data showed consistent trends towards higher attack casualties with larger attack forces, which is explained by the presence of more targets.

While we did not attempt to speculate on the precise reasons for the orders of degradation found, our independent analysis in comparing tactical trials and live fire showed similar figures to those found separately by Marshall. His reasoning may point in part to the rationale for this, that is an unwillingness to take part in the battle and this includes the use of unaimed fire from a safe position. Another possible cause cited in discussion has been that of defenders not being in a position to engage the enemy. However, the analysis considered infantrymen in low level actions where assessments of effective defence strength were based on descriptions of deployment (or on defence prisoners taken) and so that not being able to engage cannot be considered a significant factor. In view of this, the coincidence of values for non-participation with Marshall's interview data does appear to point to unwillingness to take part as being the main factor.

A comparison of these results with Marshall's quite separate interview based assessments is tabulated below:

Figure 3.13
Comparison of Estimated Effectiveness (The Marshall estimate for machine guns also includes automatic rifles and other heavier infantry weapons)

Marshall's Post Combat Interviews (Participation)	DOAE Analysis (Degradation)	Weapon Class
15%	10-12%	Rifles
15%>,<25%	17%	Machine Guns

The orders of magnitude of many of the factors are large, far larger than could have been guessed. However, it is wrong to assume that defence small arms fire is necessarily ineffective; it is as effective as it ever has been and what this analysis was designed to do was to help quantify its effects. Thus, the average rifleman in battle, in the absence of attack artillery and AFVs, can be expected to contribute about 0.5 attack casualties in the course of defending against a 3:1 attack force ratio. This is about 10-12 per cent of the average machine gun contribution (four casualties per machine gun). Moreover, the evidence points to this being made up of one rifleman in eight inflicting an average of four casualties and the remainder contributing nothing. This in itself raises a number of questions. One is over the employment of riflemen in defence and an alternative option might be to adopt the long established German practice of keeping a significant portion of the defenders as an immediate counter-attack force. Another is even more fundamental, namely the process by which armies select their infantrymen, something which has not been subject to much investigation.

That said, the analysis above has derived simple working machine gun equivalents in casualty infliction:

9 rifles (or personal weapons) = 1 m.g.

1 medium mortar (81mm) = 3 m.g.

Hence, the equivalent m.g. of an infantry force for casualty infliction in close combat is

(No. of Rifles/9) + (No. of m.g.) + (3 x No. of Medium Mortars)

Thus, for an infantry section of 8 riflemen and one machine gun the degradation is made up of 8 weapons at 1/9 degradation and one much more effective weapon, equating to 9 rifles, at 1/6 degradation. Therefore the mean section degradation per weapon over field trials in terms of equivalent live fire rifles is:

$$\frac{8 + 9}{(8 \times 9) + (9 \times 6)} = \frac{17}{72 + 54} = \frac{1}{7.4}$$

This ratio, as estimated from the three main comparisons, was 1:7.2 for open country and from subsequent analysis, see Chapter Four, 1:6.0 for urban and 1:7.6 for woods (the latter two varying with estimates of experience for the attack force).

Overall these represent a very robust confirmation of the degradation phenomenon and its order. They are based on separate trials in different areas and comparisons with approximately a hundred battles in each terrain type. This consistent factor and the asymmetry of the simulated infantry battle also sound a caution on the lessons to be derived from exercises with simulators. In these, the attackers close on the defenders, using simulated suppressive fire aimed at keeping heads down, but whose effectiveness in this cannot be measured with any confidence. The defence, on the other hand, fires its weapons directly at the attackers, whose casualties can be precisely identified with the weapons simulation kits. The result is that the effectiveness of the defence can be exaggerated by up to approximately seven times, ie the value of the degradation factor. This causes those using simulators to overrate defence and underestimate attack and counter-attack.

Once the result of the initial small arms comparison had been accepted and the capabilities of an approach by HA appreciated, further questions were agreed for study as a background to the DOAE field trials programme. In the anti-armour and armour field there was a requirement to compare weapons effectiveness in field trials with live combat. Without this, the incorporation of merely small arms degradation in combat models would bias their results in favour of other weapons systems. More immediate, however, since field trials were already being conducted, was the need to establish the variations of small arms effectiveness in the defence of woods and urban areas.

SOURCE NOTES

[1] Balchin, Brig N M Memorandum to DTI 15 Sept. 1945. Copy held in HA/dstl Library

[2] Oct 1945 paper entitled *Battle Morale*. Copy held in HA/dstl Library

[3] Foreman, Sir Denis *To Reason Why* p200 Deutsch, London, 1991

[4] Marshall, S L A *Men Against Fire: The Problem of Battle Command* University of Oklahoma Press, 2000 (latest edition)

[5] *Commentary on Infantry Operations and Weapons Usage in Korea*, Op. Res. Office, John Hopkins Univ-MD 1951 (since published. Latest edition *Infantry Operations and Weapons Usage in Korea* National Book Network, US, 1988)

[6] Spiller, Prof Roger J SLA *Marshall and the Ratio of Fire* Royal United Services Institute Journal Winter 1988

[7] Keegan, John *Gunning for 'SLAM'* Daily Telegraph 1989

[8] Dorward, Capt J C *et al Opposition encountered on the British Beaches in Normandy on D-Day* Army Operational Research Group Report No 264, National Archives (Kew) WO291/246

[9] *The Effects of Artillery Fire on Enemy Forward Defensive Positions in the Attack on Geilenkirchen* 2 ORS Report No 22 and *Fire Support on Operation VERITABLE – Effect on Forward Defensive positions.* 2 ORS Report No 26. Both are reproduced in Copp,T(ed) *'Montgomery's Scientists': OR in Northwest Europe: The Work of No 2 ORS* Laurier Centre for Military Strategic & Disarmament Studies, Wilfrid Laurier Univ, Waterloo, Ontario, Canada, 2000.

[10] Dorward, Capt J C *The Morale Effect of Bombardment* AORG Memo 635 National Archives (Kew) WO 291/246

[11] AORG Report No 292 *Comparison of British and American Areas in Normandy in Terms of Fire Support and its Effects* National Archives (Kew) WO 291/270

CHAPTER FOUR
Further Infantry Combat Trials and Historical Analysis

Urban Combat Exercises

Opposite and overleaf: Schematic model showing how urban internal combat was studied by observing combat on a single floor constructed as a stage set with overhead viewing gantries (and CCTV) for observation and umpiring

The Kings Ride series of infantry urban combat trials was put in train in 1982. They covered combat both within and between buildings, but because of the difficulties in representing very close range combat within buildings, the study was divided into two phases. The first covered individual house clearance and was at infantry section level. It took place in buildings especially erected at DOAE itself. Weapons simulators were equipped with close-up lasers, allowing for engagements down to a range of one metre. Practice grenades were used in conjunction with Simfire umpire guns. There was also very extensive close circuit television coverage of each room of the building so that we could closely monitor exactly what happened. The film was used to reconstruct the actions against time in post-trial analysis. We began with some pilot scenarios to test the systems and then went on to conduct 78 house clearance scenarios.

The data obtained from the house clearance scenarios was then applied to the 'external' urban combat trials, since to attempt to simultaneously monitor what was happening outside the buildings and within them was too complicated. One finding, which was to be expected, was that effectiveness grew with experience. This was measured in terms of exchange ratios (attack casualties divided by defence casualties), see Figure 4.1.

The exchange ratio proved a more meaningful measure than the proportion of defenders knocked out, because in trials they tended to fight on until 'killed'. Each battle was also halted at an arbitrary end point. The effect of experience therefore appeared to be another influence on combat effectiveness.

Before moving on to the external trials, we conducted some initial historical analysis into World War 2 urban combat in North-West Europe and Italy to provide a comparison with the field trials

data. It simply compared attack and defence casualties and yielded a surprising result, which is shown logarithmically in Figure 4.2. Attack casualties were on average 0.28 of those of the defence.

Figure 4.1
Urban-house clearance:
effect of experience

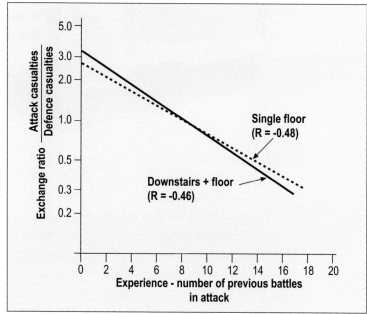

Indeed, as the broken 1:1 line shows, there were no instances of them reaching parity. This was in contradiction of the accepted wisdom that the attacker is likely to suffer more than the defender in this type of fighting. No explanation was evident at this stage, nor was the mechanism of such a surprising relationship substantiated. However, given this trend, it could be that battles with counter-attacks - temporarily changing the attackers to defenders - confused the picture unless the casualties in the two

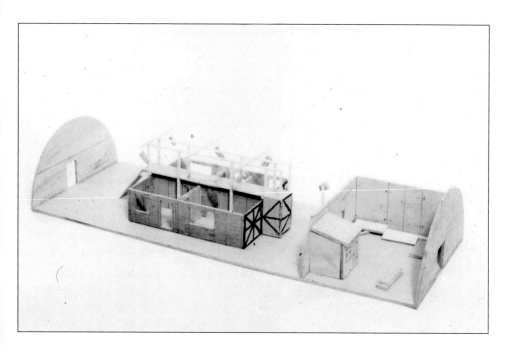

phases were separated. Hence, battles with inseparable counter-attacks were not included in the historical analysis. They are, however, discussed further below.

The urban combat trials proper took place on the Ruhleben training area in Berlin. Again, there was a pilot phase, followed by the trial proper, which consisted of 27 scenarios pitching a company against a platoon. Scenarios included tanks and APCs on each side and direct fire interactions and engineer activity, including mines and demolitions, were also represented. Casualties, ammunition use, and time data taken from the house clearance trial were adapted as rules, to be applied when the attackers entered a building. A description of one of the scenarios is given at Appendix A. The experience factor was not, however, applied and was tested afresh so as to provide two separate data sets. In particular, the defence platoon and attack company were changed from time to time. We found that there was no detectable benefit from defence experience, when measured against attack casualties per defender, and a slight but insignificant benefit for the attacker.

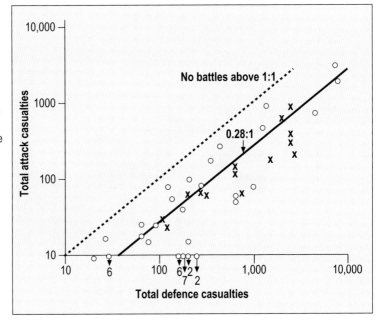

Figure 4.2
Preliminary comparison of urban battle casualties.
Key: 0 = based on full published casualty data: x = only attack casualties and defence POW data available (defence killed estimate as 1.25 x attack casualties from other data) (Numbers with arrows on the X axis represent cases of several points at very close values)

Opposite:
Air photographs of former British urban training area in Berlin (Ruhleben) used for external phases of DOAE Urban Combat trial Ex KINGS RIDE V (1984-85)

THE STRESS OF BATTLE

THE STRESS OF BATTLE

Chieftain tank of 14/20 Hussars showing SIMFIRE destruction Pyrotechnic during Ex KINGS RIDE V

Opposite:
Chieftain tank of 14/20 Hussars in urban camouflage advances in Ex KINGS RIDE V (Rulleben training area)

FV 432 of 1 Royal Hampshire Regt (fitted RARDEN turret), with SIMFIRE fitted for Ex KINGS RIDE V

Twenty of the attack scenarios employed Warsaw Pact tactics. These emphasised the need for speed and to push on, rather than clear every building of the enemy. In pursuance of this attack, infantry will attempt to motor through and use artillery fire and/or direct fire by AFVs to destroy resistance. An initial infantry attack, if needed, would be from the line of march. If this failed, the force would regroup and mount attacks with company size storm groups using simple drills. The other seven scenarios employed NATO fire and movement, with one element providing covering fire for the other as it moved. Military observers considered that the Warsaw Pact attacks were more effective. We attempted to make a comparison of the two types in terms of exchange ratios, but the NATO sample was too small for a significant difference to be detected and the best that could be deduced was that NATO and Warsaw Pact attacks had similar exchange ratios when the attackers in each type had equivalent experience.

The concept of the mini-battle package within the overall battle held good, with individual house clearances representing some of the former. For infantry in a built up area these were naturally

Attacking infantry of 1 Royal Hampshire Regt with DOAE observer pause in shelter of a building on Ex KINGS RIDE V (man at right has been 'hit' and disabled)

shorter range actions than for armour in open country. In the urban battle there were at least three types of mini-battles - static fire fights, assaults (usually with covering fire), and house clearances. The overall battles were generally longer than the equivalent open country attacks, especially those using British fire and movement tactics. In spite of their greater duration, there was no evidence of greater ammunition use by either side in these urban battles. As in all three trials, individual weapon use varied widely but there was no evidence of participation being below the 90% observed in the rural trials.

Comparisons of Exercise and Live Combat Data for Urban Battles.

Turning now to a comparison of historical and trials data, the first area for comparison is that of defence casualties. As mentioned earlier, most defenders fought until 'killed' in trials battles with no more real threat than simulators, given that there were sufficient attackers to achieve this. In real live-fire battles a very different picture was apparent (Figure 4.3). Typically, three times as many defenders surrendered, or surrendered wounded, as were killed

THE STRESS OF BATTLE

or withdrew. These ratios were not sensitive to attack AFV density or force ratio, or indeed to anything except to being totally surrounded.

Figure 4.3
Defence casualties (%)

Simulated combat		Live combat
100	Killed	20
0	Wounded / POW	60
0	Escape / withdraw	20

Attack casualties in real urban European battles were also examined for the effect of force ratio and attack tanks. We divided the battles into groups by the tank density, that is attack tanks per defence machine gun, and plotted attack casualties/defence equivalent machine guns against infantry force ratio (Figure 4.4). 'Defence equivalent machine guns' were calculated as the number of defence machine guns which would be expected to cause the same attack force casualties as the mix of weapons (rifles, machine guns, mortars) actually used under the same conditions. Each graph shows a significant trend with force ratio, the gradient of which, as the graphs are plotted on logarithmic axes, corresponds to the index of force ratio, which represented the fact that attack casualty infliction per defence weapon was proportional to force ratio to the power of 0.5. These independent sets yield very similar powers of about 0.50, lower than the value for open-country battles, which was 0.685, and indicated that attack casualties are less affected by force ratio in urban attacks. The pattern of offset or vertical shift of these four curves with tank density is broadly as expected from the rural data and is considered below and overleaf.

The average relationship of casualties to force ratio (from Figure 4.4) was used to reduce all battles to unity force ratio to test for the effects of AFV density, now using all 73 available historical examples (Figure 4.5). Here, as in the equivalent open country analysis, 'casualties/defender' is plotted against 'attack tanks/ equivalent defence machine gun', taking the same attack tank dilution factor as derived in the rural study for the effect of defence anti-tank

Figure 4.4

Effect of force ratio on attack casualties/defender

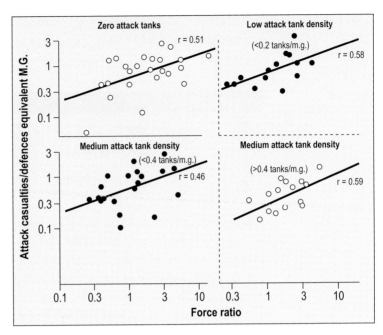

guns. These results also show a significant suppressive effect from the use of attack tanks, giving a further reduction in defence effectiveness. The general trend can be compared with that from rural battles; it is the same order of effect, a result which has surprised many.

The comparison also allows the absolute casualty values for rural and urban defence to be compared - urban being 60% less effective with no attack tanks. Conversely, the assault on Heesch by the Grenadier Guards on 25 September 1944 provides a very good example of the effect of tanks in support of the attack.

Following the loss of two tanks accompanying patrols entering Heesch, a plan was made to capture the eastern half of the village. The attack was to be made on a two company, two squadron front, all from the Grenadier Group of the Guards Armoured Division. It was preceded by a short artillery concentration to distract the enemy attention. The Grenadier history[1], describing the attack says "the attack started and went on with all the smoothness of a company rehearsal exercise on Salisbury plain ... The tanks moved forward slowly with the infantry spaced out between them, and

Figure 4.5
Effect of attack tanks on defence infantry effectiveness (at 1:1 force ratio)

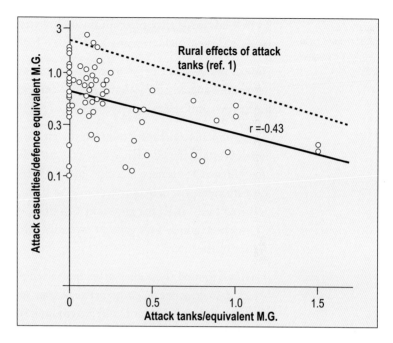

Rural effects of attack tanks (ref. 1)

r = -0.43

Attack casualties/defence equivalent M.G.

Attack tanks/equivalent M.G.

Figure 4.6
The assault on Heesch; 1st and 2nd Grenadier Guards, 26 September 1944

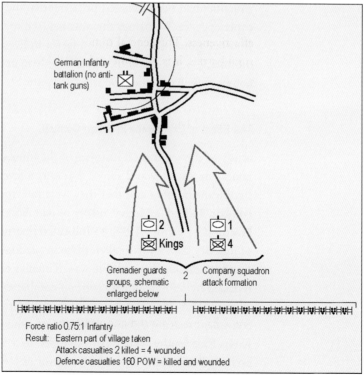

German Infantry battalion (no anti-tank guns)

2
Kings

1
4

Grenadier guards groups, schematic enlarged below

2

Company squadron attack formation

Force ratio 0.75:1 Infantry
Result: Eastern part of village taken
        Attack casualties 2 killed = 4 wounded
        Defence casualties 160 POW = killed and wounded

as they advanced they fired almost uninterruptedly with small arms and their main armament of 75mm high explosive shells."

Whilst the expenditure of ammunition was high, there was little return fire and "the bewildered enemy emerged from ditches, hedgerows and cellars to surrender in large numbers."[1]

The company/squadron groups in the attack gave a high ratio of about 2 attack tanks/defence machine gun (30 attack tanks against an estimated 15 defence machine guns). There were very low attack casualties at below 0.2/equivalent m.g. or 0.04/defender (6 casualties inflicted by 15 machine guns and 145 rifles, equating to a total of 31 machine guns). This gave an exchange ratio of over 25:1 in favour of the attack.

Having explored these effects, we now attempted a comparison of attack casualties per defender between trials and live urban battles at an equivalent force ratio and at zero tank suppression. This revealed that while the trials had shown that between 2.0 and 3.8 casualties had been inflicted per defender, the range varying with experience, in live battles this was reduced to 0.51 casualties. In other words, the degradation factor in live urban battles was 3.8 to 7.2 times, the latter figure exactly matching that for rural combat involving rifles and machine guns.

The Effect of Experience in Urban Combat.

Study of the regimental histories of the units involved in urban attacks in World War 2 shows that only a few battalions made a significant number and that they were interspersed with rural combat. Indeed, a limited survey of battalion level operations in North-West Europe 1944-45 indicated that no more than 10% of infantry combat had taken place in predominantly urban areas. Furthermore, unit experience was diluted as casualties were replaced by reinforcements with no combat experience. Making allowance for these factors, it was estimated that the mean equivalent starting experience was approximately three to four Kings Ride battles, which corresponded to a 3:1 trial casualty exchange ratio. This differed by a factor of 6 from the live battles,

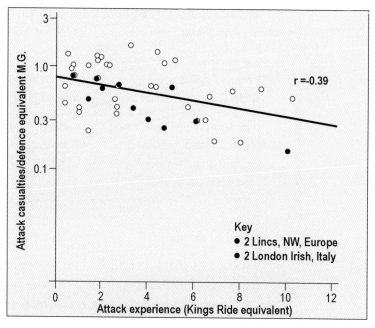

Figure 4.7
Effect of attack experience on defence infantry effectiveness (at 1:1 force ratio, zero attack tanks)

in close agreement with the rural figure of 7.2 from an independent set of data. A separate comparison with the much smaller sample of low level house clearance operations for which historical data is available on compatible experience, yields a similar order of difference.

The question now was whether the experience factor could be derived directly from historical data. The sample of this had been extended after a pilot study to include those sets where battalions fought urban battles without significant replacement of casualties, and which could be traced through unit war diary data. A measure of attack experience was taken as the Kings Ride trials equivalent battle, when each company clears one platoon position.

The results are shown in Figure 4.7 for a total of 42 of the 73 live battles used previously. Two battalions, 2nd Lincolns and 2nd London Irish, had sufficient experience to give a comparison and this showed that there was a degree of benefit from experience, while the combined set shows a significant trend.

For comparison, we could now bring forward the previous trials curve for experience and the results were confirmatory both in

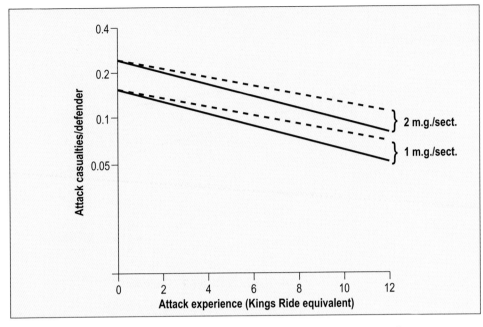

Attack experience (Kings Ride equivalent)

2 m.g./sect.

1 m.g./sect.

Attack casualties/defender

Figure 4.8 -
Effect of attack
experience on defence
infantry effectiveness
(at 1:1 force ratio,
zero attack tanks).
Key: - - = urban trial
corrected by rural
degradation; - = live
combat

Opposite:
Figure 4.9
Effect of attack
experience on defence
infantry effectiveness
in Burma (1:1 force ratio,
zero attack tanks)

Figure 4.10
Comparison of Burmese
urban with other data
sources for effect of
attack experience (1:1
force ratio, zero attack
tanks, 1 M.G./section)

order and in effect of experience, a very robust confirmation in view of the independent derivation of the two sets:

Another set of historical data also supports the effect of attack experience. A set of 24 village and urban battles in Burma, mainly during 1945, was analysed in the same way, and showed a similar effect. Figures 4.9 and 4.10 illustrate this, with a very similar order of attack casualties and a similar but lesser effect of experience. The notable difference for this set (not shown) was the insensitivity to attack AFV density. It is as yet unclear whether this was due to the type of building found in Burma, or to either side's tactics, or, and more probably, because of the confounding effects of air attacks which were identified in subsequent analysis.

Thus, analysis of real attacks has shown a similar pattern of benefit from experience to that demonstrated in exercises. This suggests that experience of attacking during exercises can be expected to yield similar improvements in subsequent combat to those shown in the exercises. In other words, it reinforces the benefits of thorough and realistic training in the attack. The mechanism of this benefit can be explored by turning to the trials data and

THE STRESS OF BATTLE

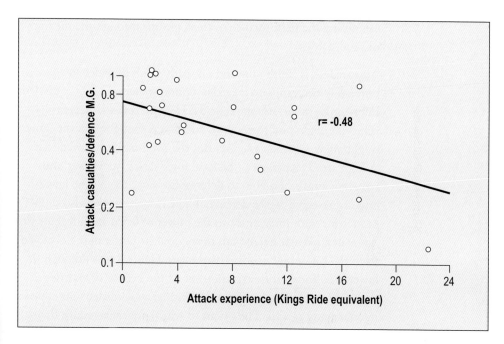

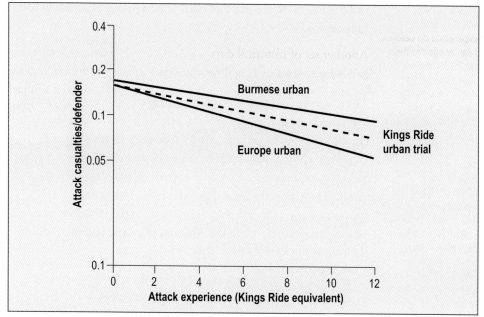

examining the performance of small groups through the medium of mini-battles.

This analysis is continuing and one early result provides an interesting contrast with attackers' optimum behaviour in equivalent mini-battles in the armoured battle. Here the attacker benefits by achieving high local force ratios and it was thought that the same might apply to urban warfare. But the mini-battles showed that at high attack experience, the local force ratios were lower, thus reducing attack casualties to defence fire since there were fewer targets presented to the defence. These casualties were also shown to increase with force ratios to the power of 0.55, an independent figure in good agreement with the equivalent power of 0.5 obtained from the full-scale historical battles (see Figure 4.4). Although the lower local force ratios explain some of the benefit of experience, they are not the whole answer; individual attack behaviour appears to contribute as well. The extent to which attackers reduce their vulnerability and increase the lethality of their fire can be investigated from the exercise data, although this has not yet been fully explored.

Summing Up the Effects in Urban Combat

These figures lead to the estimates in Figure 4.11 for both attack and defence casualties for 100 infantry in defence, with six combinations of force ratio, attack force, attack training and support included. An attack by unsupported infantry at 1:1 force ratio results in defence casualties over three times those of the attack, reducing to twice at 3:1 force ratio. Heavy attack AFV support can be expected to reduce attack casualties below one-fifth of those of defence, while the addition of attack training reduces them to below one-tenth.

To sum up, it appears that the balance of these battles is consistently in favour of the attackers with exchange ratios below 0.5:1 and capable of reduction of about 0.05:1. The corollary appears to be that successful defence of urban areas is best achieved by light or false defence and by counter-attack and that this practice will be

Figure 4.11
Typical urban battles expected casualties (company size defence)

Force Ratio	Attack Force	Attack Casualties (killed and wounded) 1 m.g. Section	2 m.g Section	Defence Casualties (killed and POW and wounded)
1:1	Infantry Only	16	24	80
3:1	Infantry Only	27	40	80
1:1	Heavy Tank Support (no def A-Tk)	3	12	80
3:1	Heavy Tank Support (20 tanks) (no def A-Tk)	5	20	80
1:1	Trained Attack - Infantry Only	8	12	80
1:1	Trained Attack - Heavy AFV Support	2	6	80 (of 100 defenders)

aided by the use of armour in support and by interactive training in the attack role. Some samples of such a posture which had to be excluded from the above analysis are the 1941 Vichy French counter-attacks on the British in the Syrian towns of Kuneitra, Merdajoun and Mezze, and German counter-attacks on the Allies in Maltot, Chaumont and Sivry in France 1944. In each case the initially successful attack was repulsed, or in some cases swamped by a hasty tank/infantry counter attack, which caused the attackers far more casualties than in the original attack. It is clear that in these urban battles the bulk of the original attack force casualties came with the counter-attack phase (although the precise breakdown is not available), and that these were 50-90% of the attack infantry strength.

Combat In Rubble (or destroyed Urban Areas)

A different development was to explore the previously neglected special area of the effects of rubbled urban areas - how much was caused by bombing and shelling, what effort was required to clear routes through it and what effects it had on subsequent combat in terms of casualties and rates of advance. Two complementary studies were initiated. One was on the HE required to cause destruction, the resultant rubble volume, and the effort required to clear routes through the rubble, while the other examined the changes to urban combat brought about by rubble. The casualty part of this comparison was straightforward, given the available casualty relationship, although it did require a new set of urban battles to be studied.

The previous analysis, based on largely non-rubbled urban areas, provided an empirical estimate of 0.62 attack casualties per defence mg. However, as three of that set of 73 total, or 42 with experience live battles, had been in rubbled areas, a further correction to the 0.62 was necessary to correct it to the non-rubble case,* reducing it to 0.61 approximately. The equivalent geometric mean of the new set of 9 battles in rubble was 0.94 attack casualties per defence mg, with a standard ratio of 1.53.** This provides an estimate of increase in attack casualties in attacking through rubble by a factor of approximately 1.55, a difference significant of the 5% level.

Two comments can be made on the results of this comparison.

a. The geometric mean increase in casualties by a factor of 1.55 turns out to be close to the factor of 1.65 estimated for the effect of major obstacles and prepared obstacles in open country battles.

b. The standard ratio of the result for fighting in rubble is the lowest encountered with urban data or attack casualties; this may reflect the more homogeneous nature of combat in rubble than in undamaged urban areas of various geometry.

A summary of the Standard Ratios for the casualties per defensive weapon as progressive analysis of close combat has occurred is tabulated in Figure 4.12.

---

* Two had neutral effect by their removals, the third was estimated to cause a 2% reduction in the geometric mean of the remainder in the area of data being compared.

** Standard Ratio: A measure of the dispersion of results about a mean. In this case it means 68% lie between 1.53 x the (geometric) mean and 1/1.53 x that mean.

THE STRESS OF BATTLE

Figure 4.12
Table Residual
Variability of Attack
Casualties/Defence
Weapons with
Progressive Analysis

Conditions	Standard Ratio
Urban combat, raw data	2.3
Urban combat analysed for effect of force ratio and suppression	1.95
Urban combat analysed as above plus experience	1.80
Urban combat in rubble as above	1.53
Flat open country analysed for force ratio and suppression	1.4

The other part of the comparison between rubbled and non-rubbled urban areas concerned advance rates. This needed data sets to be found with and without rubble and the vast majority of cases were fresh. It also required a spread for each set over a range of force ratios, up to the maximum, which approximates to an attacker being unopposed. These sets also represented a variety of attack experience states. However, rather than face the large historical task of building samples to enable experience to be tested, the more economical alternative of correcting for experience on the basis of the combat trials data was used. The data so corrected appeared to give consistent relationships.

The effect of German parachute infantry defence on the above results needs to be considered, however. In the famous urban battles in Italy - the Canadian assault on Ortona in December 1943 and the battles for Cassino Town in early 1944 - the defence was provided mainly by parachute units, and the attackers frequently referred to the qualities of their opponent as one reason for their problems. In addition to these two, the defence of Rees am Rhein during the First Canadian Army closing up to the Rhine in February 1945 was also based on parachute troops. Thus, four of the main battles (two different days of the Allied attacks at Cassino were used) in the sample featured troops of a particularly good qualitative reputation. We therefore needed to establish whether the performance of the paratroops was above the German mean for defence effectiveness.

We did, however, identify a different machine gun allocation to German parachute units than to their other infantry.* This could make a defence force seem more effective, man for man, to an attacker and the different weapon mix was allowed for in the initial calculations. As a simple check, the sample of nine rubble battles used earlier was broken down by extracting the four mainly parachute regiment defences. The residual subset of five showed a greater mean than the overall set - 1.06 casualties per mg, instead of 0.943 for the overall set, not significantly different. Thus, there is no question of the German parachute troops' effectiveness exaggerating the effect from rubble. We then plotted the unopposed advance rates against force ratio, using simple linear scales in Figure 4.13.

Starting with the ceiling value of unopposed advance rates, the two sets, without rubble and with rubble, produced limited samples which show mean rates of advance of 756 and 394 metres per hour respectively, showing that the attacker will progress half as fast through rubble as through relatively undamaged urban areas. Where the attack was opposed, high force ratios did not make a significant difference, but at a given force ratio it did slow the advance by a factor of 7. While mobility is a factor, perhaps more significant is the fact that featureless rubble will disorientate an attack force, especially when it receives fire and goes to ground and has to locate from where the fire is coming.

* The different German Infantry units in WWII had different establishments and in particular varying numbers of machine guns. A comparison of the total mgs in a battalion with the total of men in the rifle companies is made below. It shows that, with the exception of the armoured Panzer Grenadier battalion, the parachute battalion had the highest ratio of m.g. to rifle company men.

	Battalion M.g. per man in rifle coys	Defence effectiveness as mean equiv. Rifles/man
Pz Gr (armd)	1:4.3	2.86
Parachute	1:6.9	2.16
Infantry ('44)	1:7.8	2.02
Pz Gr (mot)	1;8.2	1.98
VolksGrenadier	1:11.9	1.67

Thus for example parachute battalions if manned by equivalent men would expect to be 7% more effective than the 1944 Infantry division and almost 30% more than a VG Division.

Ref: Handbook of German Military Forces 1945 US War Draft Technical Manual TM-E 30-451

THE STRESS OF BATTLE

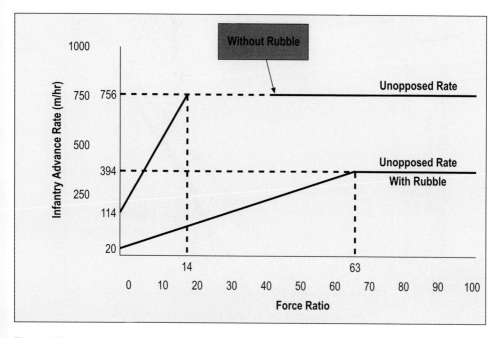

Figure 4.13
Schematic Diagram
of Infantry Advance
Rates in urban areas
(at experience two
battles)

Close Combat in Woods and Forests

We now turned to fighting in woods. This study followed both
the open country and urban area studies and was also carried out
after the equivalent combat field trials (Ex. Kings Ride III). It took
a different approach, building on the experience of the previous
studies and trials and of the other effects identified in them.
In outline, a major data collection phase built up a sample of a
hundred and twenty battles in woods and jungle, ranging from
the US Civil War to the Korean War. Preliminary analysis of subsets and of the total set explored the relationship between attack
casualties per defender and force ratio. Following this, variability
was reduced using battle descriptions and data to reduce each factor
to a pooled standard simple battle, for analysis. The equivalent
simple battle itself had the summed forces of the separate mini-
battles and the total equivalent defence weapons, weighted by
type according to open country HA. These were weighted by the
number of mini-battles in which they were used. This resulting
set of simplified data was tested by multivariate analysis for all
measured and hypothetical effects.

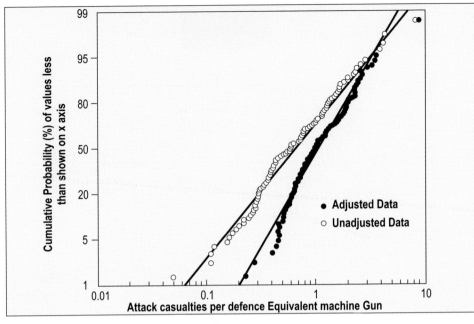

Figure 4.14
Normal cumulative distribution for attack casualties at one-to-one force ratio reduction in variability when effects of statistically significant factors are removed

Having derived the best estimates of these factors, including types of support, ambush, surprise, weather and times of day, the variability of results about the mean was reduced as in Figure 4.14 above. The closer to vertical, the better is the agreement between results. The gradients indicate that the standard ratio fell from 2.7 to 2.0 from this analysis, ie that instead of 68% of results varying between 0.37 and 2.7 times the geometric mean, this range reduced to 0.5 to 2.0 times the geometric mean, almost halving the range of values.

Attack Casualties per Defence Equivalent Machine Gun

A comparison of fighting in woods with fighting in the open and in an urban environment was then made:

Figure 4.15
Comparison of Fighting in Woods with Fighting in the Open and in an Urban Environment

	Fighting In		
	Woods	Open	Urban
Attack Casualties per Action per Defence Equivalent Machine Gun at: 1:1 Force Ratio	0.818	2.07	0.76
Ratio with Woods at: 1:1 Force Ratio	1	2.5	0.93
Force Ratio Power Relationship	0.418	0.685	0.50

At a 1:1 force ratio, infantry defending in woods were assessed as being 2.5 times less effective than when defending in the open. This figure increased to 3.4 when the force ratio was 3:1 in favour of the attacker. Our conclusion was that the reduction of defence effectiveness in woods was primarily because of the limited fields of view, and hence the restricted ranges of fire. When fighting in woods was compared to fighting in an urban environment, the levels of infantry defence effectiveness were similar over a wide range of force ratios. This indicated the same problems with fields of view and fire. The force ratio power relationship, which determines the influence of force ratio on attack casualties, also showed that woods and urban fighting had a closer relationship than either did to fighting in open country. This produced a set of results consistent with those for open and urban terrain, but some factors did produce different effects. Thus, degradation was greater for night battles and lesser for artillery suppression, as well as different for machine guns.

The Effects of Experience in Woods Combat.

As we had done with open country and urban battles, we then went on to examine the question of attacker experience. Because of the complexity of the observed interaction with the cumulative effects of casualties, this was tackled by auxiliary analysis. We selected battalions belonging to 53rd (Welsh) Division during the 1944-45 campaign in NW Europe, since they were involved in a series of battles in wooded areas. We were also able to allow for the incorporation of casualty replacements, whose combat experience was low. As seen in Fig 4.15 below, the effect of experience of woods fighting in the Kings Ride trial was very similar to that experienced by this division in 1944-45 overleaf.

The effects of attack experience can be compared from the results of urban and woods analysis for both trials and live battles as in Figure 4.16 overleaf.

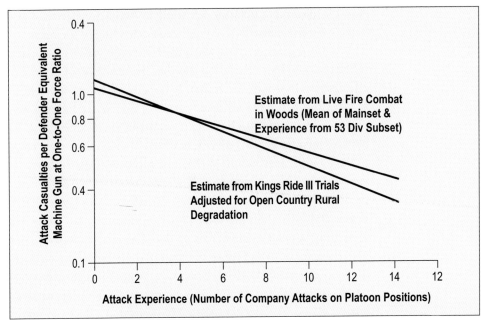

Figure 4.15
Effect of Experience
on Combat in Woods
Reduction in Infantry
Attack Casualties
with Increasing
Attack Experience
after Adjusting for
Replacements in
Combat. Comparison
for Wooded Terrain
of Combat and Trials

Figure 4.16
Number of Prior
Company Attacks
on Platoon defence
positions needed
to halve Attack
Casualties

	Woods	Urban
Combat Trials	8.3	10.5
Live Combat	10.7	9.7

The results are remarkably consistent, especially given the different manifestations of casualties and their effects in trial and in live combat, and the different levels sustained in each due to combat degradation, which applied to the live combat case. Typically, troops with no previous experience needed to carry out some ten such attacks to gain the experience required to halve their casualties.

Ambushes, a type of woods fighting which was reflected in the Kings Ride trials, was not subjected to historical analysis. More recently, ambushes during the Malayan Emergency 1948-1960 and Borneo 1963-66 have been added to the database, however, and this type of combat could benefit from further study, including its sensitivity to other factors such as surprise and combat degradation.

THE STRESS OF BATTLE

Combat in Areas of High Relief

During the analysis of infantry combat we found that some forces appeared more effective in defence in mountains and in areas of high relief, both by measures of casualty infliction and resisting an enemy advance. A separate study of unopposed advances by infantry had identified and assessed variation in movement as being linked to height variations on the route. However, the effect of slowing at an obstacle had previously been assessed as causing a significant increase in attack casualties, so could the separately assessable slowing effect account for the increased attack casualties in areas of high relief?

No trials comparison had been possible and the general approach was to consider the effect of terrain relief as overlaid on that for terrain cover. In other words, we tested the relief effects of fighting in wooded hills as a multiplier to the flat terrain expectation for woods. We recognised, too, that warfare in mountains and other areas of extreme relief presents opposing forces with a variety of interrelated problems concerning logistics, trafficability, command, control, and communications, deployment, etc. This means different tactics from open country. There is a widespread perception that the defence of mountainous terrain confers significant advantages on the defender, though no quantified evidence supporting this view was available. Previous historical analysis had, however, suggested that the relative slowing of movement over hills allows the defence additional time to engage the attacker.

We therefore proposed a hypothetical relationship between the elevation of a defence and an increase in defence effectiveness, measuring the difference between the maximum and minimum elevation traversed by the attacking force. This could be obtained from maps and had a number of advantages:

   a. Correlation with the degree of exhaustion inflicted on troops; hence the amount of delay to be expected whilst exposed to fire.

b. Close correlation with the local gradient encountered by the attacking forces, again helping to indicate the degree of delay to be expected whilst exposed to fire.

c. Ability to 'fine-tune' the elevation measure for different assaults, and different directions of assault, within the same area.

d. Ease of definition and measurement.

Yet, we realised that looking at peak elevation in isolation was unsatisfactory, since it did not reflect the physical difficulties that infantry had in traversing the terrain. For instance, it did not take into account that they might be operating on a high but level plateau. Consequently, we had to take into account local peak and trough values. This also had the benefit of reflecting the broken nature of extreme terrain since, at a higher altitude, the ground over a given separation is likely to be more rugged and impassable. However the larger the area selected, the greater the peak/trough variation and range. Moreover, the use of local peak/trough values made it impossible, without a significant additional amount of historical research, to distinguish between the starting positions, objectives or ground traversed by infantry operating in the same area. Nonetheless, when the positions of the forces involved were uncertain, and the peak/trough differential encountered by the assaulting infantry was unknown, this was used as the default value.

Measuring local gradient directly was suggested as being truer to the original hypothesis. However difficulties in identifying what constituted a local maximum gradient and acquiring such data for all the battle sets were considered impracticable on the grounds of cost and this also was discarded.

Our previous work on advance rates had established an empirical relationship between a non-mechanised unopposed advance rates and the elevation of terrain and had developed a relationship between advance rates and force ratio for a given defence effectiveness. Hence, a relationship between defence effectiveness and attack force change in elevation of terrain was indirectly inferred.

THE STRESS OF BATTLE

Similarly, the relationship between advance rate and defence effectiveness in casualty infliction was derived from earlier historical analysis studies of a sequence of opposed advances on generally level ground at infantry battalion/brigade level over several days:

$$\text{Defence Effectiveness (by advance rate)} \sqrt{} = \frac{a\ \text{FR}}{\text{Advance Rate}} \qquad \text{Equation 2}$$

Where the advance rate is measured in miles per day, a is a product of factors including the degree of air superiority and mechanisation of the advance, and FR is the force ratio of attackers per defender.

If it is assumed that opposed advance rates are affected by elevation in the same proportion as unopposed advance rate then Equation 1 (see footnote)* can be substituted into Equation 2, and a defence effectiveness multiplier defined as follows;

$$\text{Defence Effectiveness Multiplier} = \frac{\text{Defence Effectiveness (by advance rate)}}{\sqrt{\text{Force Ratio}}} = \frac{1}{\sqrt{1 - e^{-50/h}}} \qquad \text{Equation 3}$$

This effectiveness and elevation equation was hypothetical and unproven, given the small amounts of data previously available for mountain warfare. It was therefore now necessary to assess the extent to which this equation accurately represented variation in defence effectiveness with elevation, as well as identifying the factors involved.

The main analysis used attacker casualties to calculate the defence effectiveness. The secondary method of analysis used advance rates instead of casualties to calculate the defence effectiveness, in order to confirm the principal findings. Both methods involved calculating 'raw' defence effectiveness, and then comparing with that predicted by the hypothesised relationship between relief and defence effectiveness.

---

* Analysis of a separate sequence of unopposed advances further showed that advance rate was related to changes in elevation traversed by forces according to the exponential relationship given here):

Unopposed Advance Rate $= a\ (1 - e^{-50/h})$ Equation 1

Where h is the height differential of attack movement in metres as described above.

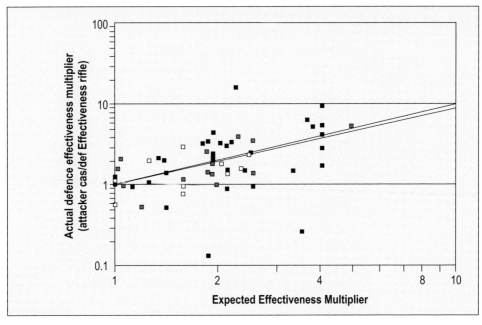

In order to test this hypothetical relationship between relief and combat effectiveness, actual defence effectiveness relative to that on level ground was plotted against the hypothesised defence effectiveness enhancement due to relief, as set out above.

A line representing the ideal hypothesised defence effectiveness multiplier* can also be drawn to provide easy comparison with the actual defence effectiveness line. This grey line has a gradient of 1, and an intercept on the response variable axis equal to the level ground effectiveness of the defences under consideration. With no modification due to elevation, the hypothetical effectiveness of the force should be the basic defence effectiveness. The difference between the ideal and actual gradient of the line will determine any factor necessary to bring the hypothetical effectiveness described by Equation 1 into line with the actual observed effectiveness.

It was found that a log/log relationship gave a suitable basis for comparison. This is consistent with the log normal variation found in effectiveness measurements. Log/log plots of defence effectiveness

---

* Multipliers were 1 for flat ground; 2 for 200m variation between peak and trough;
  3 for 400m peak to trough; 4 for 800m peak to trough.

adjusted for force ratio and AFV/Artillery suppression against the expected enhancement due to relief were drawn for:

a. Each set of results, here divided for comparison into independent sets by defence force nationality and by data collection (CDA and other sets). This provided a suitable sub-division to test the consistency of the separate sets of data, in addition to the overall set.

b. A regression line for the pooled results against the hypothetical relationship.

Each of the 63 points represents a single battle. The actions themselves covered Italian defensive actions during World War 1 in northern Italy and in Africa and Kephalonia in World War 2, German defences in North Africa and Italy in World War 2, Korean actions in the Korean War, French defences in France in World War 2, and British and US defences in North Africa and Italy also during World War 2. They were selected according to the following criteria:

a. The attack is a clearly distinct event in time and area. This criterion is necessary to remove those cases with a duration in days or with no intervisibility across the battlefield.

b. The defence controls the local high ground and the attack seeks to gain control of this ground through a direct action. This assumption is necessary to ensure the defence gains the full benefit of the gradient in slowing a direct attack rather than infiltration.

c. The attack is both vigorously pressed and resisted. This is necessary to avoid unrepresentatively low results given, for example, by early defence withdrawals or envelopment attacks.

d. There is no counter-attack or extended contest with repeated exchange of control of the position.

e. The defence force is deployed on the feature rather than mainly on the reverse slope, so that the attack is engaged whilst encountering elevation obstacles.

Figure 4.18
Agreement of Data for
Different Nationalities,
Defence Effectiveness
at Elevation with Ideal
Trendline.

As will be seen in Figure 4.17, the grey line of the hypothesised relationship is drawn for comparison with the data set regression lines. It has a gradient of 1, and originates at (1,1); for effectiveness in combat on level ground. The empirical gradients of the individual sets agree well, as indicated in Figure 4.18, although some show wider confidence limits due to small samples.

Data Sets Country	Data Source	Points	Correlation Co-efficient Squared (r2)	Significance of Correlation	Gradient ± 95% Confidence Limit
A	Combined	25	0.24	1%	1.01 ± 0.79
B	Combined	7	0.46	5%	0.87 ± 0.87
C	Other	4	0.03	>5%	0.49 ± 3.89
D	CDA	15	0.38	1%	0.85± 0.86
E	CDA adjusted and unadjusted	12	0.14	>5%	1.19± 2.03
All Data		63	0.27	0.1%	0.96± 0.40

The pooled results show that the mean gradient of the combined set gives very good agreement with a gradient of 0.96 as opposed to a hypothetical gradient of 1. This is very unlikely to have arisen by chance.* Thus, using the new samples of battle data to test the hypothesis, it was confirmed for casualty data, the associated test on movement rates (not shown) was also supportive.

The series of separate studies described in this chapter had extended the analysis of infantry close combat from open, predominantly

* The confidence limits for gradient demonstrate that although a relationship between combat effectiveness and elevation exists, there is considerable uncertainty about the gradient. More validated data, particularly at extremes of elevation, is required to narrow the confidence limits of the gradient. The combined trendline gradient may vary between 0.56 and 1.36. However this is strongly influenced by two outlying points in the Country A defences, and one in the Country E defences. If these are excluded then the gradient confidence limits narrow to ± 0.28, to give a gradient of between 0.68 and 1.24

flat, country to closer (urban and wooded) and to more rugged terrain. They had shown a robust family of relationships including consistent combat degradation in the different terrains, but also special features associated with each.

The next step was to return to the armour/anti-armour battle. This had to be approached in a rather different way to much of this combat study, but was to reveal some intriguing findings, especially in terms of combat participation.

SOURCE NOTE

[1] Nicolson, Capt. N and Forbes, P *The Grenadier Guards in the War of 1939-1945 Volume 1: The Campaign in North West Europe* pp144-147 Gale and Polden, Aldershot, 1949

CHAPTER FIVE
Armour and Anti-Armour Combat Effectiveness Studies

Once the small arms degradation factors identified in the initial HA studies had been generally accepted, the need for derivation of comparable estimates for armour and anti-armour systems became apparent. However, this area was a more complicated one to explore, rendered more so by the variability of the small battles for which data was available. Initial simple analysis was not found useful in collapsing data and establishing relationships.

Furthermore, while good tentative trials data was available from Exercise Chinese Eye and other trials, including in the USA, this was from a different era to that of the combat data in terms of weapons systems. In particular, there was no way in which direct comparisons could be made between the conventional World War 2 anti-tank gun and the anti-tank guided weapon systems used in the trials of over three decades later. In the previous study, combat degradation factors for small arms were assessed by comparing their performance in real combat with that achieved in tactical field trials. This was possible because analysis had shown that the effectiveness of rifles and machine guns in close combat had changed little over the years. That this was patently not true for anti-armour weapons meant that a different way of measuring anti-armour combat degradation other than comparison with field trials needed to be developed.

Anti-Tank Guns in Defensive Combat

In essence, the approach adopted was to study historical anti-tank battles as a personal 'interest' outside the work programme, which itself dealt with the more tractable elements of the project. It was hoped to return to HA with whatever new insights might eventually be provided by the extramural historical investigation. It was necessary to start with battles which involved only one type of anti-tank weapon and the study concentrated on defence because experience gained from the small arms study suggested

that combat effectiveness is easier to study in defence. Two actions in which anti-tank guns were in combat largely on their own against tanks were initially selected. Both came from the campaign in North Africa and concerned British anti-tank guns.

Before going any further, it is worth providing some information on the British Army's anti-tank gun organisation during World War 2 and the types of weapon used. Both the artillery and infantry employed anti-tank guns. The anti-tank regiments Royal Artillery came under divisional control and initially consisted of three batteries, each of 12 guns, but later changed to four 16-gun batteries.* Conventional infantry battalions (post-1940) included an anti-tank platoon, initially six guns but later increased to eight. The more mobile motor battalions, which were part of armoured divisions, had a complete anti-tank company of sixteen guns. They often deployed with an anti-tank battery RA under command.

Any account of the usage of the World War 2 British anti-tank guns themselves must be set against the evolution of their design, and their use against the intended targets – Axis tanks. In the early part of the war as a whole, and until mid 1942 in the Western Desert (shortly after the first battle of el Alamein in July), the main British anti-tank gun was the 2 pdr. This gun was adequate against Italian tanks and the lighter German tanks (Pz I and II). At anything but short range it was ineffective against the German medium tanks (Pz III and IV), which progressively replaced the lighter tanks in the armoured formations.

The 2 pdr was eventually replaced, mid 1942 in the Desert and early 1943 in Tunisia, by the 6 pdr whose introduction had been delayed for production reasons. Anti-tank artillery and motor battalions were re-equipped first. When introduced, this was a match for contemporary tanks and, with improved ammunition, was effective until the end of the war, although its frontal performance against the heaviest German tanks was inadequate. It remained the main towed anti-tank gun in infantry battalions, but artillery anti-tank units progressed from solely towed 6 pdrs to a mixture of heavier guns, both towed and self-propelled 17pdr guns. These were significantly superior in performance, but their heavier weight meant that different tactical concepts had to be introduced. The three guns are shown, all at the same scale, below.

* For a few months in 1942, anti-tank regiments were broken up, their batteries being incorporated in field regiments RA. This change was reversed by the end of the year.

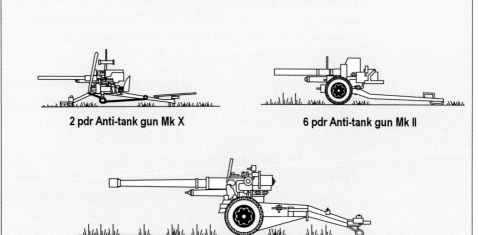

2 pdr Anti-tank gun Mk X

6 pdr Anti-tank gun Mk II

17 pdr Anti-tank gun Mk I

The characteristics of each gun were:

Gun	Shot weight	Calibre	Penetration		Carriage weight	Crew
			500 yds	*1000 yds*		
2 pdr	2.4 lbs	40mm	52mm	40mm	1845 lbs (0.837 tons)	4
6 pdr	6.25 lbs	57mm	79mm	65mm	2698 lbs (1.24 tons)	5
17 pdr	17 lbs	76mm	200mm +	113mm	6700 lbs (3.04 tons)	6

In the early actions against Italian tanks in the Desert the 2 pdrs (and the less effective 37mm Bofors) proved adequate and played a key role in trapping the retreating Italian Tenth Army at Beda Fomm in early February 1941, halting a series of tank attacks. As recounted later in this chapter, they were mostly used as mobile guns on portees. In the static role their limited performance was soon exposed by the German tanks, which were able to stand out of range and engage them. Nevertheless, if the crews could take up suitable positions and hold fire until the attacking tanks were within range, the 2 pdr guns could be effective. The Australians successfully used them in this way at el Alamein in July 1942, although by then they were obsolete. The history of the 2nd/3rd Australian Anti-Tank Regiment records:

> "Eight enemy tanks attempted to cut off our infantry positions. Two 2 pounder guns on the flank were manned by Sgt K Digby and Bdr A S Muffett. Bdr Muffett, who commanded the forward guns, realised the seriousness of the position and allowed the enemy tanks to come almost on top of his gun before opening fire. His gun then quickly knocked out three Mk III German tanks but the fourth scored a direct hit on the gun, killing the layer and wounding all of the crew, including Muffett. The enemy tanks then changed direction and came within the arc of Sgt Digby's gun which, from a defilade position, destroyed four more, at which the remaining tank withdrew."[1]

Major Rainier RE, writing during World War 2, described the Australian approach to tank hunting using 2 pdrs:-

> "In the rear of their forward positions the Aussies would construct a number of cleverly concealed pits each holding a two pounder and a couple of men… The tank hunters would crouch invisible in their shelters…only when the tanks were within two hundred yards would the hunters open fire with single aimed shots."[2]

When the 6 pdr was issued it offered anti-tank units the chance to engage effectively without the necessity of holding fire until at very short range. Some units had little opportunity to train on it before they found themselves facing the German Gazala offensive at the end of May 1942. however. By the time of the fighting at el Alamein fighting at the beginning of July 1942, these 6 pdrs (part towed, part on portee), were beginning to play a significant part, complementing 25pdrs in the direct fire anti-tank role.
In the to and fro of this battle several small anti-tank actions took place. They include a notable defence by the Australian 2nd/28th Battalion Group. British tanks were unable to get through to them, and only eight guns (three 6 pdr and five 2 pdr) had reached the newly taken battalion position when they were counter-attacked

by German armour. The guns succeeded in knocking out eight tanks and two armoured cars on the overrunning German force. The battalion history mentions :

> "One gun on the right flank was served by the BSM (Warrant Officer A A McIlrick MM) and two other men, until it was finally blown out. The heap of 19 used 6 pounder shell cases in the shallow gun pit and the semi-circle of six knocked out German tanks were still there four months later and tell their own story of courage and gallantry against overwhelming odds."[3]

The battle of Alam Halfa in August 1942, which marked the final defeat of Rommel's Alamein attacks, is normally described as an armoured brigade action, but operationally was actually one of most important 6 pdr anti-tank gun defensive battles. The German hook was met by 22 Armoured Brigade in a planned counter penetration position on the Alam Halfa Ridge. In addition to its three armoured regiments, this brigade also included the 1st Rifle Brigade (1 RB). While most accounts dwell on the role of the tanks of the armoured regiments, the sixteen dug in anti-tank guns of 1 RB, placed in front of the tanks, are less frequently mentioned.These guns, holding fire to 300 yds range, claimed 19 tanks hit, five by one gun. Major General Roberts who commanded the brigade for this battle acknowledged the anti-tank claim of 19 and estimated an overall brigade total of 30.[4] This implied a substantially lower contribution by the average tank (there were 166 present) than by the average gun, an observation to which we will return.

Of the First Army defensive battles in Tunisia, several featured 6 pdr actions. It was here that the 17 pdr made its combat debut, although its use was limited. After North Africa the need for anti-tank weapons declined as most Allied operations were offensive and anti-tank defence was mainly needed to resist German counter-attacks.

Detailed Battle Studies

With regard to the initial two anti-tank battles selected for detailed examination, both concerned 6pdrs in the static role. The first was the so-called Snipe action during the break-in phase of the decisive British assault at el Alamein. It involved 2nd Rifle Brigade, a motor battalion commanded by Lt Col Victor Turner, supported by a battery of 76th Anti-Tank Regiment RA and a small detachment of Royal Engineers. In total, Turner had nineteen 6pdr guns and his task was to seize and hold a piece of key terrain on Kidney Ridge until the arrival of an armoured brigade, which would then exploit forward, using the ridge as an anchor. The action began on the night 26/27 October 1942 when the Battalion moved forward to take up position and ran into the leaguer area of a German battle group. Even so, 2 RB was able to establish itself and soon found itself engaging Axis armour. The expected armoured brigade did appear but withdrew in the afternoon after suffering losses. The riflemen continued to fight on until shortly before midnight, when, with no prospect of relief, the survivors withdrew. Subsequent analysis of the battlefield revealed that 32 Axis tanks had been destroyed, together with five self-propelled guns, and that a further 15-20 knocked out tanks had been recovered by the Axis. All but one of the anti-tank guns had either been destroyed or rendered inoperable and Turner's force of 300 men had suffered 25 per cent casualties.

The other action took place five months later, when the British Eighth Army had crossed into Tunisia after pursuing Rommel the length of Libya. Rommel had combined with von Arnim in an attack on the Allied forces in western Tunisia in February and then turned to deal with the threat to his rear posed by Montgomery. Forewarned by Ultra of Rommel's intentions, Montgomery prepared a defence based on minefields, artillery, and anti-tank guns. On the morning of 6 March 1943 Rommel duly attacked with three Panzer divisions. The main thrust came up against 7th Armoured Division, which had two infantry brigades deployed forward. The study itself concentrated on the performance of the anti-tank guns of 131 Queens Brigade, which faced 15th Panzer Division, 201

Guards Brigade, facing 21st Panzer Division, and 5 New Zealand Brigade, which was opposed by 10th Panzer Division. By the end of the day all Axis attacks had been repulsed and they withdrew at last light. It was Rommel's swan song in North Africa; he handed over his command to von Arnim two days later and left the theatre.

In both cases it was possible to obtain detail on the performance of each individual anti-tank gun. Two additional studies – attacks by British armoured brigades on German defences at el Alamein in July and November 1942 – proved less useful since the defence data was not so detailed. On the other hand, smaller scale actions by British, Australian, and New Zealand anti-tank guns during the abortive April 1941 campaign in Greece did provide meaningful information.

Analysis of the data produced a new insight in terms of anti-tank gun combat degradation. It came from the recognition of the role of "heroic performance", which was well described anecdotally in individual accounts but began to mean more once the achievements of those recognised by gallantry awards began to be quantified. Ignoring this aspect left widely scattered results; including it provided a means of overcoming a major problem in assessing comparative performance. It is, however, worth mentioning that heroic performance by the many has long been the implicit assumption in much combat modelling. This disregards the fact that there is an understandable absence of universal heroism in the real world and that combat degradation, rather than heroism, is the norm.

The method devised, after examining combat performance, used the hypothesis that heroes, defined as those who received gallantry awards, would perform to their physiological limits and their weapons' physical limits and could thus provide the baseline against which the performance of the majority could be compared. Throughout this study the estimated quantitative values of combat degradation are the values of the factors by which baseline performance needs to be multiplied. This estimate of combat degradation is, of course, conservative, in that the performance of heroes might not match the performance which could be achieved in tactical field trials situations; also because the significant difference in combat performance was found to be when at least one of the crew (or *de facto* crew) received an award. Thus, the baseline includes guns manned by crews below normal establishment and crews of which only one member's performance fulfils the criteria for heroes. Nevertheless, as will be seen, this does provide a significant division of weapons into two groups by effectiveness, and, although conservative, offers estimates of major combat degradation.

Study of the actions indicates that at the most between 20% and 30% of guns were manned by heroes. In addition to gun crews, these include heroes who were commanders at platoon, (anti-tank) company and battalion level who were present during the action and either participated in, or took over, the firing of the guns. It is worth citing some individual heroic performances. In the battle of Medenine in March 1943, Sgt I Andrews of 1/7 Queens won the Distinguished Conduct Medal (DCM) for the use of his 6pdr gun to engage an enemy force of about 18 tanks, killing a total of at least 8 tanks. Quotations describing his role state that, after awaiting opening fire until 5-6 tanks were within 1000m and killing 5 of them, he became involved in a duel with the survivors. His platoon commander, describing the heavy enemy fire, said:

> "This fire was very heavy and not one unwise head was to be seen above ground during this outburst. Nevertheless Sgt Andrews took up the challenge… Sgt Andrews ordered his crew to take cover whilst he continued to load and fire the gun himself. He disabled two further tanks…".[5]

Sgt Crangles, another member of 1/7 Queens, also won the DCM for the handling of his 6pdr while facing another part of the same attack. This gun saw off four separate attempted assaults during the day, together with fire by the German tanks. Its confirmed total claim was 14 tanks killed before the gun was disabled by a direct hit on the recuperator. The Brigade's War Diary records that:

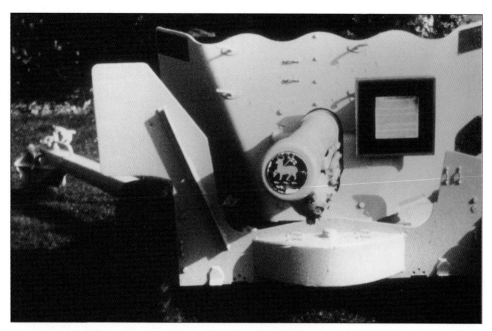

"…but for the determined conduct of this gun crew, there is a good chance that the enemy might have lifted the mines and broken down the wadi. There is no doubt that the gallant fight

Closer view of the destroyed tanks
(PHOTO: MAJ E G SANDYS WHO AS CAPT SANDYS, ANTI-TANK PLATOON COMMANDER, TOOK THESE PHOTOGRAPHS)

put up by this gun was a determining factor in stopping an initial breakthrough at this point".[6]

In the Snipe action during el Alamein in October 1942, Sgt Charles Calistan won the DCM for his use of his 6 pounder in an attack by 8 tanks and several self-propelled guns. Under heavy enemy fire, Colonel Turner, Major Bird and Corporal Francis redistributed ammunition from knocked out guns. An improvised team of Col Turner as loader and observer, Lt Toms as Number 1 and Sgt Calistan as firer disabled 5 tanks and one of the guns in the first engagement but this almost expended its ammunition. Lt Toms dashed 100 yards in his jeep to fetch more ammunition but the jeep was set on fire on the return journey, 10 yards short of the gun. Ignoring the flames, Col Turner and Lt Toms unloaded the ammunition and ran back to the gun. Sgt Calistan then knocked out the other 3 tanks with successive shots at a range of less than two hundred yards.*

---

* Calistan already held the Military Medal. Turner was awarded the Victoria Cross for his outstanding leadership and Bird received the Distinguished Service Order. In addtion, two further DCMs were awarded, as well as ten Military Crosses and Military Medals for those involved with the anti-tank guns.

THE STRESS OF BATTLE

Campaign/ Battle	Heroes			Others		
	Total Guns Deployed (and in combat)	Total Gun Engagements	Tanks Hit per Target per Gun Engagement*	Total Guns Deployed (and in combat)	Total Gun Engagements	Tanks Hit per Target per Gun Engagement*
Greece (several)	8	8	0.40	38	44	0.054
Alamein 2RB at Snipe	10	25	0.15	23	27	0.048
Medenine Queens Bde	2	7	0.43	22	38	0.027
Medenine Gds + NZ Bdes	6	9	0.39	14	14	0.12
ALL	26	49	0.275	97	123	0.052

Figure 5.1
Anti-Tank Gun Combat
Performance: Mean
Number of Tanks Hit
per Target per Gun
Engagements

* For example in one engagement, if a gun has 10 targets and hits 3 in that engagement then a figure of 0.3 hits per gun engagement is calculated. The mean for several engagements is the average of these rates.

Quantifying the Effects of Heroism

The detailed results from reconstructions of these actions, including Greece, are summarised in Figure 5.1 above. Here the performance of heroes and 'others' is compared in terms of the numbers of enemy tanks hit per target available per gun engagement. This normalisation to hits per target is based on DOAE trials results which indicate that rate of fire is proportional to target availability. It is also a better way of comparing the performance of individuals than using, say, targets hit, because it takes account of target opportunity. The cumulative distributions of hits/target/gun engagement for Medenine, Snipe and Greece are shown in the table. Most attention should be paid to the median or 50% values; for example 50% of non-heroes achieved just over 0.03 on the performance scale, whereas 50% of heroes achieved approximately 0.3, or 10 times, as many casualties.

Thus, the table provides two broad estimates of the extent to which heroes participated in anti-tank battles. It shows that 26 out of

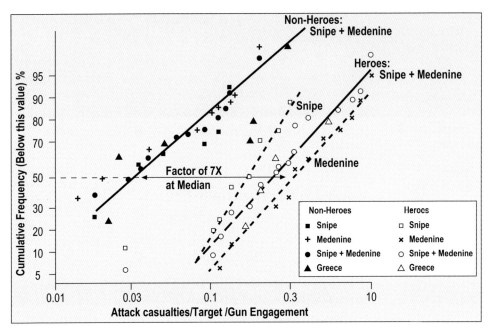

Figure 5.2
Battles Studied in
Detail Attack Tank
Casualties/Target/Gun
Engagement for Anti-
Tank

149 guns deployed, that is 17%, were fired at least once by heroes and heroes took part in 49 out of 172 engagements, that is 28%. It also demonstrates very clearly the higher combat performance of the heroes, whose guns achieved 0.275 target hits per target per engagement compared to only 0.052 by others. This difference is highly significant statistically and is well illustrated by the separate battle analyses (see Figure 5.2 above).

Using the hypothesis that heroes are those not subject to combat degradation it was now possible to make a simple and conservative estimate of overall combat degradation. On the assumption that the performance of about 20% of deployed anti-tank gun personnel is not degraded, then the performance of the other 80% is degraded, by an average factor of 0.052/0.275 = 0.19. This gives an overall mean degradation factor of 0.2 x 1 (heroes) plus 0.8 x 0.19 (others) = 0.35. The conclusion from these figures is that performance by anti-tank gun crews in battle is only about one third of what could have been expected had they performed to the limitations set only by their weapons' characteristics.

The base axis of Figure 5.2 represents level of performance, while the vertical axis indicates how often the different levels are achieved.

For example the 'non-heroes' line indicates that this group achieved 0.03 attack casualties per target gun engagement on only some 40% of occasions and less than 0.1 on almost 90% of occasions. By contrast the pooled 'heroes' line shows that group achieved 0.1 on approximately 10% of occasions (or more than 0.1 on 90% of occasions). The median 50% value shown on graph indicates that the two groups differed by a factor of about seven times in killing performance.

Wider Surveys of Anti-Tank Combat

This simple estimate of combat degradation is conservative, not only because of the hypothesis that heroes are not subject to degradation, but also because the sample of battles examined here could be biased in favour of successful defensive anti-tank battles. This could lead to an overestimate of the proportion of heroes. To obtain a more widely applicable estimate it was necessary to examine overall performance in a wider sample of battles, including some in which defence positions were overrun. These widened the scope by covering defence by a mixture of anti-tank and field guns (the former being predominant) and by a mix of anti-tank guns and tanks. Some German defensive actions were also included, but accounts of these are usually less detailed than those of British and Commonwealth actions. In all, 43 actions were examined in detail and a general survey was made of a further 81 battles.

In addition, some tentative estimates of tank combat degradation were made. However, in any assessment of the relative value of tanks and anti-tank weapons from combat data, there is a fundamental problem in that, whilst casualties to both types of weapon have been recorded, the type of weapon responsible for each casualty has not. For tank versus tank battles empirical relationships between casualties and force ratios had been derived, but to extend this procedure to include tanks and anti-tank guns of disparate morphology, and with differing crews, a further empirically determined factor 'T' had to be introduced for guns. Essentially this was used to modify the gun quality index to the scale of tank quality index, allowing for the effect of the extra qualitative factors which differ between the two classes weapon. A detailed explanation of how the 'T' factor and 'quality products' were developed, together with examples, is at Appendix B.

With regard to the heroism aspect, the initial phase had demonstrated the possible significance of gallantry and value of officers and SNCOs in supervision but only in the two battles studied in detail. The variation in effectiveness between other battles which were studied in less detail was greater than that within those two detailed battles. Was this due to variations in the incidence of heroism or gallantry? Clearly, the hypothesis would have to be tested on a much wider sample of battles than the highly successful defensive actions of Snipe and Medenine. For this broader investigation, methods would have to be devised that were far less labour intensive than those used to set up the initial hypothesis. We extended our Western Desert samples of battles to cover nearly all major British anti-tank defences, including a variety of tank and anti-tank and field gun mixes, anti-tank guns both in ground role and on portee in a mobile role. A comparison of the 'T' factor of anti-tank guns manned by heroes and that attained by anti-tank guns in the wider sample was also used subsequently to estimate the proportion of heroes to non-heroes. This made it possible to extend the range of battles over which combat degradation could be assessed.

The first estimate of tank/anti-tank gun equivalence, by the method outlined earlier was made using data from "unbiased" sets of World War 2 Western Desert tank/anti-tank battles. These were unbiased in that, unlike Snipe and Medenine, they included unsuccessful as well as successful defences. As the analysis proceeded, more data became available and estimates of the 'T' factor in defence (T_D) were also made for a number of North European battles. These were:

a. Actions in Normandy in 1944 involving a total of one hundred and twenty seven 75mm and 88mm German towed anti-tank guns attacked by British and Canadian medium and cruiser tanks armed with 75mm (75%) and 17pdr (76mm) (25%) guns.

b. Seventeen separate actions during the 1944-45 North-West Europe campaign involving a total of forty-nine 75mm and 88mm German towed guns attacked by Sherman tanks of 3rd and 4th US Armoured Divisions, with a mix of 75mm and 76mm guns.

c. Thirteen separate actions during the German counterstroke at Mortain in August 1944 involving 27 guns and twenty-one actions in the Ardennes (December 1944) involving 38 guns. In both cases 57mm and 76mm US towed anti-tank guns were attacked by German Pz IV and Pz V Panther tanks and SP guns, all essentially armed with types of 75mm gun.

The cumulative distributions of both defence and attack 'T' factors obtained from the Western Desert set of battles are shown in Fig 5.3.

Figure 5.3
Distribution of Anti-Tank Gun 'T' factors from mixed Anti-Tank Battles in the Western Desert

Note: The 'T' factor represents the empirical multiplier to be applied to a towed gun factor (calculated as for tanks) to represent its equivalent casualty causing capability to a tank. For the German 50mm PAK 38 anti-tank gun the calculated factor is unity so 'T' also represents the tank equivalence of this gun. For British guns calculated factors are 0.96 for 2pdr, 1.56 for 6pdr.

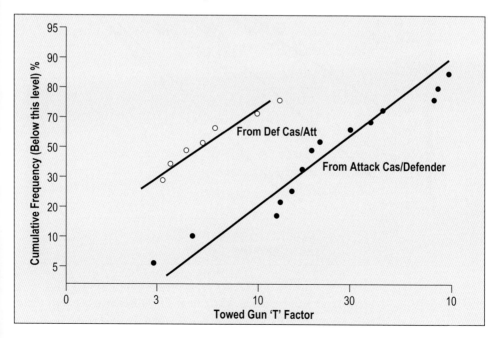

T_D varies between 3 and 95 for individual battles and has a (geometric) mean of 23. Fig 5.3 is similar in format to Fig 5.2 but with the alternative measure of gun performance, the T factor, on the horizontal axis.

Before going on to consider the results of the analysis of the NW European battles, Snipe and the battles in Greece, it is of interest to compare the "unbiased" Western Desert results with those obtained from the successful defensive battle at Medenine. This is done in Fig 5.4, which shows the cumulative distributions of T_D for the Medenine battles alongside the Western Desert results. As might be expected, the mean value of T_D, which can be considered to be a measure of the effectiveness of anti-tank guns in defence, is 30% lower in the Western Desert battles, although this difference is not statistically significant. This could be used to revise the previous degradation estimate by comparison with the same set of heroic performance figures, however further improvement in this is dealt with after more detailed analysis below.

Figure 5.4
Comparison of Defence Anti-Tank Gun 'T' Factor Distributions, Separating Medenine Battles

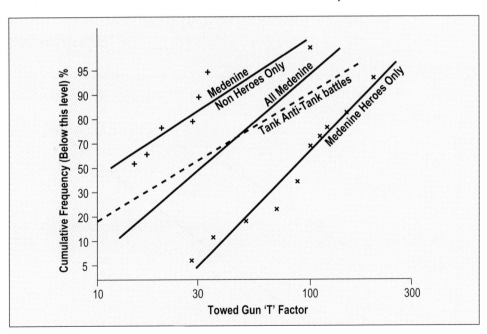

Also shown in Fig 5.4 are the separate distributions of T_D for heroes and non-heroes at Medenine. The difference between these two curves, by a factor of between 5 and 6, confirms the findings of the analysis of individual performance. The (geometric) mean value for T_D was calculated from each of the above data sources and was found to be consistent across all theatres of operation.

For those battles in which only tanks participated, it was possible to obtain a fairly accurate estimate of the performance of tanks in the defensive role measured in terms of attack casualties per defending tank. A defence composed of tanks alone was less effective than defence by towed anti-tank guns alone or a mix of anti-tank guns and tanks. On the assumption that tanks in a mixed defence inflicted casualties at a rate no higher than that commonly achieved in a tank-only battle, the apparent kill rate of the guns appeared to be roughly three times greater than that of the tanks, despite the relative disadvantage of guns in terms of mobility, protection and traverse.

It was found that this disparity between the performance of tanks and guns could be related to the different crewing of each, and in particular to the higher density of officers and SNCOs with deployed anti-tank guns. It was shown that this could be due partly to the higher incidence of heroism from those higher ranks.

The above analysis took into account the characteristics of both different tanks and anti- tank guns by means of the quality product and the 'T' factor. A simpler, empirical, analysis which ignored the quality of the different weapons was possible for a number of engagements in very different terrain in Normandy in 1944. In these actions British tanks, with a 3: 1 mix of 75mm and 17pdr (76mm) guns, attacked varying numbers of German tank and anti-tank guns. There was no significant difference between the effectiveness of the two types of tank but the ratio of anti-tank gun to tank effectiveness averaged 2.55, a value which supports the results of the more complicated analysis given above.

The strong indication that anti-tank guns are more effective than tanks in defence may be surprising to many but not, perhaps, to the military historian Paddy Griffith who wrote of tank casualties that "relatively few appeared to have been caused by enemy tanks"[7] or to Lucas-Phillips who commanded an anti-tank regiment in the

Western Desert. He stated that "in tank battles the dominant weapon was in fact the German anti-tank gun" and asserted that "the anti-tank gunner, if well sited and strong of heart, really had the tank cold nearly every time".[8]

Yet, since the tank has greater protection, mobility and gun traverse, its combat effectiveness could be expected to be at least as good and possibly better than the towed gun, even in defence. That its lethal combat performance is significantly less could be for a variety of reasons:

a. The engagement process with tank crews could be linked, at some levels, to decisions over whether to engage in the first place and hazard an expensive weapon and its crew, analogous to the "Fleet in Being" concept in naval warfare in which a fleet is preserved, rather than fighting, in order to maintain its threat.

b. Additional mobility gives a viable option to withdraw a tank to safety, while anti-tank guns often had little option but to fight it out.

c. There are different modes of fighting by tank and towed gun crews. The tank presents a larger target to the enemy and hence 'jockeys' between firing positions, while an anti-tank gun relies more on concealment and firing from a flank.

d. Tanks have combat roles other than the destruction of enemy tanks.

While all of these reasons may make some contribution, the low level tactical studies described here have highlighted the value of individual gallantry in gun effectiveness and its relationship to responsibility and rank. This leads to another possible reason for the relatively high gun effectiveness compared to tanks - the difference in numbers of officers and senior NCOs to each weapon. For example, in a tank squadron there would be 16 tanks with 6 officers and 4 or 5 sergeants, that is approximately 0.65 senior NCOs (SNCO) or above per tank. In contrast, the anti-tank battery (or company of a motor battalion) had a sergeant to each gun, with a troop leader and troop sergeant in addition to a battery or company commander, and nearby infantry company commanders immediately interested in their success. This gives approximately 2 SNCOs or above per gun, a total of three times the equivalent for tanks. The difference also implies some significance in the ability of officers to move between weapons, unlike the tank officer who is confined to his own weapon system.

The effect of this high number of officers and NCOs can be illustrated by examination of a sample of identified heroic anti-tank gun crews from those battles studied in detail. The indications from this sample are that those manning guns and receiving the award usually, but not always, included the SNCO gun crew commander, whereas only 20% of awards were to a lower rank (3 corporals, 1 rifleman). In addition, in 75% of cases, an officer or NCO senior to the gun crew commander was present and supervising or helping in some way.

Because of the major importance of the effect of identified heroism emerging from the detailed analyses of Snipe and Medenine, it was clearly valuable to test the set derived from the broad surveys in order to determine the extent of this effect. In the provision of data, the complementary survey of gallantry awards to anti-tank crews has been combined to fit the attributed awards to individuals in specific actions. This allows a simple analytical comparison of awarded heroes per gun and mean effectiveness for each battle. (It is recognised that this is itself a simplification and that, for example, one hero per gun could represent three guns, each with one hero taking part, or just one of the three manned by a wholly heroic crew). The results for anti-tank defences without minefields are shown in Figure 5.5 overleaf.

This demonstrates that the results of analysis of the detailed reconstructions of Snipe and Medenine accorded closely to that of the general survey and, when pooled, revealed an increase in effectiveness from 14, when there were no heroes present, to 100.5 in the case where there was one hero per gun. This compared favourably with previous findings on the influence of anti-tank gun heroes. It also added weight to the finding that anti-tank guns were more effective than tanks in defence, with the lowest T factor

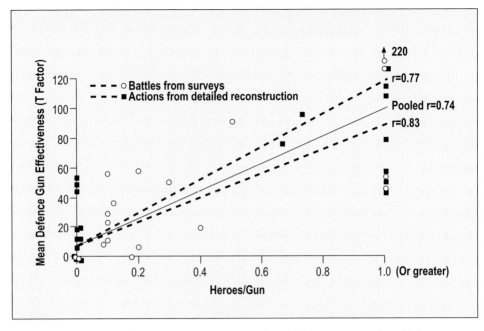

Figure 5.5
Effect Of Heroism
On Defence Gun
Effectiveness Anti-Tank
Guns Without Mines.

of 14 proving superior to that of the average tank, which was a mere 8.4.

Cases in which defensive minefields had been present were then analysed in the same way. As shown in Figure 5.6, they reveal a mean multiplier on effectiveness of twice that at low levels of heroes per gun, but drop to no advantage at the higher levels. The latter statement must be qualified, however, by the fact that it was influenced by the Medenine 'mini-battles' in which the protective minefields were small in size. The effects of minefields therefore required further study.

Another interesting parallel can be drawn from Field Artillery practice when in the direct fire role against tanks. This was something that happened not infrequently in North Africa, where swiftly moving armour outflanked or infiltrated forward positions and came up against the gun line. Once field guns were faced with an armour threat, the order "Target tanks – Open sights – Gun Control" was given. This meant that instead of the fire being controlled at troop or battery level, as was the case with indirect fire, each gun No 1 (commander) now controlled his own fire.

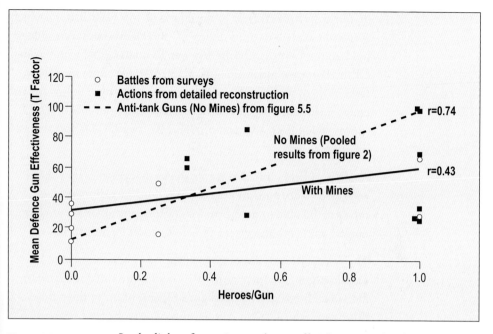

Figure 5.6
Effect of Heroism and Minefields on Defence Gun Effectiveness

In the light of experience, the unofficial practice developed for each gun to be commanded by an officer, rather than the No1, in the belief that fire could be more effectively controlled, especially in terms of selecting targets. In addition, studies of field gun actions against tanks also revealed that officers could provide greater motivation to the crews, also enhancing weapon effectiveness.

In the Western Desert, 25pdrs were sometimes purposely used as anti-tank guns until sufficient 6pdrs were in theatre. In Tunisia, the British First Army, operating in the west of the country, was critically short of 6pdrs for much of the campaign and employing field guns in the anti-tank role became almost the norm. One classic example of this occurred on 26 February 1943, the first day of an offensive by von Arnim's Fifth Panzer Army against the British sector. One of the initial objectives was Sidi Nisr, merely a small white building and primitive railway station, which acted as a patrol base. It was held by the 5th Hampshires, supported by 155 Field Battery RA, which deployed its eight 25 pdrs forward of the infantry in the anti-tank role. The Germans attacked with infantry supported by no less than 74 tanks, including the 14 of the formidable Pz VI Tiger, which made its first combat appearance in Tunisia. Thanks largely to the efforts of 155 Field Battery, which eventually had all its guns destroyed, the Hampshires were able to hold up the German advance for over 12 hours before withdrawing. Of the Battery's initial strength of 130 all ranks, only nine men (two of them wounded) escaped, but they destroyed at least seven tanks, including a Tiger, and were subsequently awarded a DSO (downgraded from VC citation), an MC, two DCMs and at least six other awards.

Analysis of field guns in this role shows that performance varies with force ratio, guns in prepared positions (detachments less exposed and able to hold firm for engagement of targets at close ranges), and with the extent of heroic action by individuals.

The mean effectiveness of guns in the open was to inflict 0.3 casualties/gun at a force ratio of 1:1 tanks/gun or 0.5 at 2:1 with individual heroically manned guns capable of up to three times this figure. The T factor comparison can also be used giving a (geometric) mean of 19.7 and a standard deviation (a measure of spread of data) representing a ratio of 2.7, similar to that for anti-tank actions.* Few of these actions include minefields, and the effectiveness of guns in those that do cannot be statistically distinguished from other actions. However, if the field gun battles at zero heroes are pooled with the anti-tank gun results the difference in T factors with mines is significant at the 5% level.

The effect of heroism can be considered in the same way as for anti-tank guns above, plotting effectiveness against heroes/gun. As with anti-tank guns this form of relationship follows the expected pattern from the analysis of detailed actions indicating that identified heroism is a major factor (see Figure 5.7 opposite). The ratio of effectiveness at zero heroes to that at one hero per gun is 1:5 which is consistent with the results from individual actions examined in detail and the pooled anti-tank gun results reported above. The T Values for gun effectiveness are also consistent with those from the anti-tank gun set T=13.5 at no heroes compared to 14.8 for "without" mines and 16.8 for pooled anti-tank guns.

---

* i.e. 68% of all cases lie between 2.7 times and 1/2.7 times geometric means.

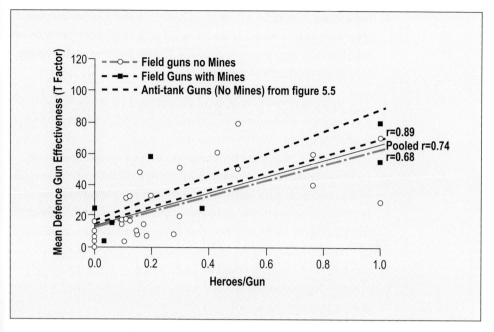

Figure 5.7 -
Effect of Heroism
on Defence Gun
Effectiveness Field
Guns in Direct Fire
Role.

The correlation coefficient is a little lower here indicating 55% of the variation is accounted for by the allowance for heroism.

Anti-Tank Guns in a Mobile Role

The final area to be explored was anti-tank guns in the mobile role. Although British World War 2 anti-tank guns had been designed as towed equipments, as were those of their main opponent the Germans, measures were taken to improve the battlefield mobility of these guns. The British mainly used modified trucks to carry or 'portee' the guns with some capability for firing from the portee vehicle in emergency. As heavier weapons were introduced and the Allies moved over to the offensive, these vehicle adaptations on portees were discontinued and indeed anti-tank weapons generally were used less frequently. The heavier guns in use by the end of the war were carried in open-turreted and tracked 'tank destroyers' based on a tank chassis. Examples are the British 17 pdr Achilles and the American 90mm M36 tank destroyer. The German use of mobile anti-tank guns evolved through the use of some mounted on armoured half-tracked vehicles, to the adaptation of obsolete light tanks as multi-role self propelled guns and tank destroyers, then to heavily armoured, non-turreted adaptations of conventional tanks as tank destroyers, such as the 75mm Jagdpanzer IV, which was based on the Pz IV chassis.

The trend to greater mobility of these towed weapons, for at least a proportion of the inventory, was thus general, The simple British portee used from 1940-43 has a useful sample of recorded combat experience in which the performance of this exposed, but more mobile weapon, can be compared with that of the basic towed gun when deployed. This comparison is not of mere academic interest. It offers the opportunity to look at the same weapon in a different morphological form and, being of direct relevance to comparisons of the performance of mobile unarmoured weapons platforms in the anti-tank battle, it could provide evidence of the battlefield combat degradation of ATGW mounted on unarmoured vehicles and even of anti-tank helicopters.

The War Office review of 'The Development of Artillery Testing and Equipment'[9] attributes the idea of transporting the anti-tank gun in a vehicle to the French, who found that the 25mm guns issued to infantry brigade anti-tank companies in 1939 were not sufficiently robust to be towed over long distances. The same principle was applied to the Bofors 37mm gun issued to 7th Armoured Division in Egypt 1939 and it was then that the idea of firing from the truck was first introduced. However the history of Rhodesian gunners indicates that the idea, and its prototype, originated in their own experiments.[10]

A War Office specification for a portee, drawn up in January 1940 agreed that "the gun should be capable of moving either portee or towed, but that firing from the vehicle was not necessary".[11] In the Middle East however, the idea of firing from the vehicle was still popular and arrangements were made locally for the conversion of a Ford 30 cwt chassis to enable it to take the shock of discharge and to allow nearly all-round traverse of the gun.

The same manual claims the method of firing from the portee had proved highly successful against the Italians and was being repeated against the Germans. Against the latter it had been found particularly successful in rearguard actions when it offered the advantage of a quick 'get-away'. Although intended for use in the desert, it is also noted that it was employed quite effectively in Greece. Here it was again used for rearguard actions, some in mountain passes. A good example was at Proasteion Ridge on 13 April 1941, when 1 Armoured Brigade was under attack and about to be outflanked by 30 light and medium tanks. A portee troop was successfully used in a counter penetration role. The accounts make it clear that the guns fired mounted "shepherding the enemy armour into an angle made by a copse in the ravine" hitting eight tanks and delaying the German Panzer spearhead. So effective was it that a subsequent German account described the troop as "a British tank division in an impregnable position".[12]

Tactical successes like that at the Proasteion Ridge reinforced the popularity of the portee concept. One anti-tank regimental commander was quoted as saying: "It is quite possible for a quick troop leader or section sergeant with an eye for country, to avoid casualties and do considerable damage by skilfully using ground and engaging tanks over open sights for a few minutes, rapidly withdrawing under cover, changing his position and repeating the dose".[13] Several actions researched for this study confirm their effectiveness in this role. On 14 April 1941, during the initial stage of the siege of Tobruk, the first significant German armoured assault was broken up by a mobile force, which included porteed guns, after being stopped by dug-in field guns. The Australian anti-tank history noted that "mobile fire, in the form of mobile anti-tank guns and tanks, was brought to bear at the vital moment when the enemy tanks were bewildered and trying to reform."[14] During Operation Crusader, the November 1941 offensive to relieve Tobruk, porteed guns were used both to harass and to provide a mobile element to static defences. A typical example of the latter was a German tank attack on the 26th New Zealand Battalion, which was supported by a battery of 25 pdrs and a New Zealand portee troop of 2 pdrs. Two of the four portee guns survived until the German tanks were in range. They kept firing and had more opportunities than the field guns to do so because "high up on their portees they were able to observe more targets

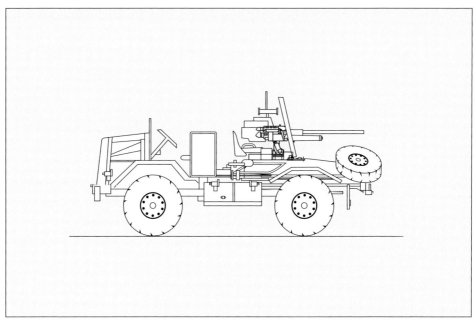

than the field gunners". By careful count of burning tanks only, it was established that the two portee guns, with some help from the 25 pdrs, had disabled the remarkable total of 24 tanks, having fired over 300 rounds in total. The troop commander Lt Pepper had, throughout the action, moved from gun to gun, when he was not scouring the battlefield for more ammunition, and "*had courage to burn*". He was awarded an MC for this action.[15]

In mid-1942 the new 6 pdr gun began to replace the 2 pdr. It, too, was provided with a portee; in this case a modified 3 ton truck from which the gun could be fired forward or backward, dependent on how it was positioned. It performed well during the fighting at el Alamein in July and August 1942, but after Montgomery's decisive assault in late October and early November, anti-tank actions became less frequent and the portee's use declined. Indeed, the official view was that "anti-tank guns will never be fired from their portees except when there is literally no time to bring them into action on the ground."[16] Even so, they were employed on occasion, usually with static guns. One example of this was the 2nd Scots Guards at Medenine. To counter the German attack the Scots Guards used a reverse slope defence, but two of its 14 guns

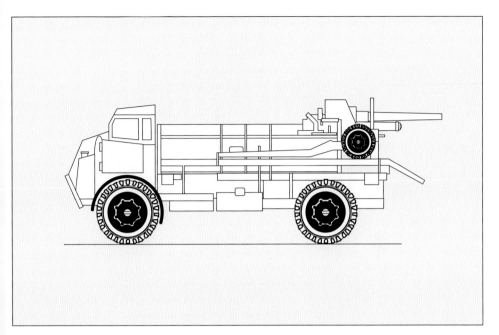

6 pdr Anti tank gun
on Bedford portee

were retained on portees. The detail of this action includes at least three sorties by their individual guns into forward sniping positions to make a more aggressive defence. For one of them, the gun commander Sgt Mutch was awarded an MM for killing a Panzer IV special at 50-60 yards range. In the adjacent 131 Queens Brigade area an anti-tank gun reserve was left on portee to move to counter penetration positions as necessary.

The final development of wheeled portees came with the Deacon mounting a 6 pdr in a turret with all round traverse on an armoured lorry chassis. Only limited numbers were provided but one mobile action at El Hamma, after the outflanking of the Mareth line in late March 1943, adds to the sample of mobile use of these guns. The 76th Anti-Tank Regiment RA was ordered to form a protective screen behind 1st Armoured Div on the approach of some twenty bypassed German tanks. Their towed guns also deployed but most had no part in an action in which eight of the Deacons stalked small groups of enemy tanks, These guns, together with four towed 17 pounders, claimed up to eight tanks, including a Tiger, and two 88 mm guns for the loss of three Deacons disabled. The general official view, however, remained

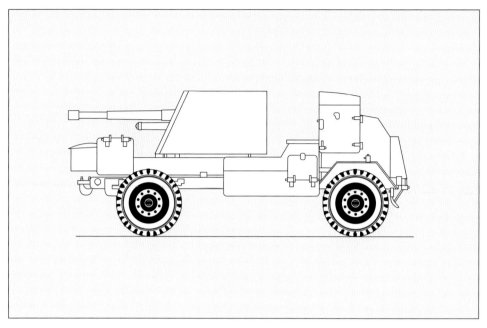

Sketch of 6 pdr Deacon

that the portee tended to be used too much like a tank, which it was not and that "as a result casualties in anti-tank units had been heavy and they had not been justified by the amount of casualties inflicted on the enemy.'[17] Analysis of the effectiveness of portees serves to question this judgement.

A total of 25 portee battles was analysed with approximately equal numbers of 2 pdr and 6 pdr actions. Each group showed very similar geometric mean 'T' factors (20 for the 2pdr and and 25.4 for the 6 pdr), so similar that the two could be merged for further analysis, despite the differences in both gun and vehicle/ portee size. The mean portee factor T of 23.4 was comparable to that for the same guns in the ground role.

The significance of heroic behaviour on performance can be seen in Figure 5.8. As for anti-tank and field guns, the expected form of linear relationship is obtained with the no hero to one hero per gun ratios of effectiveness similar to that of the other groups at 1:4.4. Thus the form of relationship is similar to that found for guns in the static role, although with a slightly lower correlation coefficient 0.74, indicating 55% of the variation explained in this case.

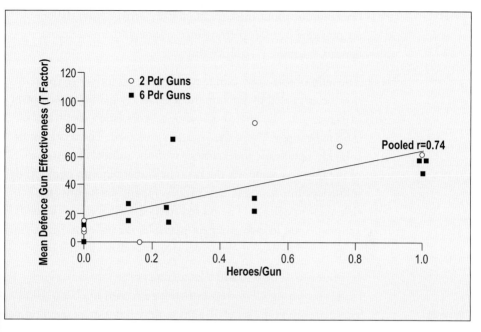

Figure 5.8
Effect of Heroism on Defence Gun Effectiveness Anti-Tank Guns on Portees

The two high effectiveness battles (at 0.25 and 0.5 heroes/gun) were both exceptional cases in which portees engaged a passing tank force from the flank. At zero heroes the portee T factor of 14.6 also represents an effectiveness greater than that of the average tank (T = 8.4).

The analysis introduced in this study had widened the general surveys to allow homogeneous sets by defending gun type, covering a substantial proportion of British and Commonwealth actions and battles. The sets created cover anti-tank guns, field guns, and porteed guns, plus one set for anti-tank guns with minefields. A major part of the variations in effectiveness of each of these four sets has been shown to be related to identifiable heroism, assessed as heroes/gun confirming the anecdotal accounts of the more heroic actions described. The difference in contribution of heroically manned guns from others and the intermediate cases are of similar order to those derived from gun performance at Snipe and Medenine. The variability of the individual gun contributions in each of these two sets (and of those heroic guns for which adequate data exists from the wider surveys) show similar distributions about these means already derived from the one set provided by trials performance, although the non-heroic appears the more variable of the two.

The ratio of these two extremes of level of performance could now be estimated by pooling the separate comparisons, as shown in Figure 5.9. The pooled data shows a correlation coefficient of 0.65 indicating 42% of the variation explained. The relationship is highly significant and, together with the mutual consistency of the four sets, supports the hypothesis that heroism significantly influences anti-tank gun effectiveness for anti-tank guns and field guns in defence. The pooled relationship represents a good approximation to each group, in particular the use of anti-tank guns in static and mobile (portee) roles give equivalent effectiveness.

It is interesting here to add a later comparison which has been made comparing US towed anti-tank guns with the US M10 SP guns, essentially the same 3" guns as towed, but in an open turret on an armoured chassis similar to that of a Sherman tank and fitted with radio. Unlike the tank-gun comparison we are here dealing with similar gun crews in/on mounts of different

Figure 5.9
Effect of Heroism
on Defence Gun
Effectiveness:
Summary of Results

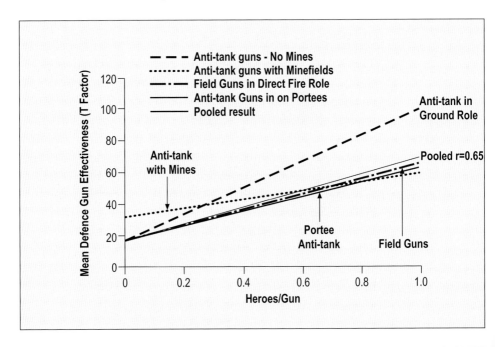

morphology. Comparison of the performance of 65 towed guns and 195 SP guns showed similar mean effectiveness (using 'T' factor again) of 28 for towed (comparable to the 27 from the larger British sample) and 24 for the SP guns. The difference is not significant and there is certainly no evidence of a physical tank killing advantage to the more sophisticated platform. This is not to say, however, that there is no operational advantage in moving an SP gun to battle, redeploying locally and getting it into action, since our comparison only considered the guns in position and able to engage (Figure 5.10).

Figure 5.10
Comparison of Anti-Tank Gun Effectiveness

| | No Individual Radio | Individual Radio | |
	British Towed Guns [1, 12]	US Towed Guns	US M10 SP Guns With Indiv Radio's
Sample (guns)	1435	65	195
Mean Effectiveness ('T' Factor)	27	28	24
Median Effectiveness ('T' Factor)	N/A	32	22

Anti-Tank Guns in Offensive Roles

There remained one more task, to examine anti-tank guns in the attack. This a less obvious role than defence, given their physical characteristics, but has occurred on a significant scale, particularly by the Germans in World War 2. They developed tactics both for their anti-tank guns and even for the large and high silhouette 88mm anti-aircraft/anti tank guns. A British report on the fighting in North Africa[18] noted that "German use of anti-tank guns, pushed right up with or in front of their tanks was a notable feature of most engagements". The use of 88mm anti-aircraft guns appears to have evolved in the Capuzzo battles in Libya in mid-1941, when these guns were deployed ahead of the tanks and inflicted major casualties on the British tanks before the German tanks could engage.[19] Although the effectiveness of the 'eighty-eight' was fully recognised by the British, the generally greater killing effectiveness of anti-tank guns was not universally acknowledged.

The British did not develop such an effective anti-tank attack role in North Africa, largely because their concept of close all arms co-operation was not nearly as advanced as that of the Germans. There were, indeed, some cases of lone British portee guns attacking and forcing Axis tanks to withdraw. More typical was the action of Major Taylor of the Northamptonshire Yeomanry, an anti-tank regiment RA, during the early part of the prolonged fighting at el Alamein during July 1942. The citation for his DSO reads as follows:

"On the 3rd of July the enemy pressure on the Alamein line showed signs of relaxing. Major Taylor was with a Troop of his anti-tank guns on a narrow commanding ridge which ran into the enemy position. Major Taylor at once seized the initiative and with his four guns advanced alone and unsupported along the ridge. "Inspired by his example and due to his orders and leadership these guns fought their way forward, slowing and skilfully putting out of action 4 enemy tanks and an 88mm gun. Having advanced 2000 yards alone they came under increasingly heavy shell fire and machine gun fire to which they had been subjected throughout the advance. Three out of the four guns had been put out of action and barely 200 yards of ground had been surrendered before the arrival of supporting troops an hour later. This action reflects the highest credit on Major Taylor for courage and leadership of a most outstanding order." [20]

Indeed, many instances of the British use of anti-tank guns in the offensive role were as the result of low level initiative.

Even so, in the majority of cases attacking anti-tank guns have been used in combination with attacking tanks, so that gun effectiveness has had to be estimated by deducting the expected casualties due to large numbers of tanks. Given the expected variability in this quantity, this leads to greater variability in assessment of gun effectiveness, even before true variations occur. Nevertheless, three subsets have been compared as tabulated in Figure 5.11 below and showing similar results, with a pooled estimate of T in the attack as 13.

A separate comparison is also possible using the small sample of four (three British, one German) gun 'alone' actions with mainly

Attack Guns	Defence force	Sample	Geometric mean T for Attack Gun
British anti-tank guns in the attack	Tanks and guns	14	15.9
German anti-tank guns in the attack	Tanks and guns	25	12.8
German anti-tank guns in the attack	Anti-Tank guns only	24	12.5
	All Pooled	**63**	**13.2**

Figure 5.11
Anti-tank gun
effectiveness in the
attack

heroic crews (close to 1 hero/gun). These have a mean value of T = 35 from which, at the same average hero density as that for defence guns, a geometric T factor mean at 0.2 heroes/gun of 0.36 x 35 = 12.5,* can be expected, which is in agreement with the estimate for German anti-tank guns on their own.

Tank And Anti-Tank Gun Comparisons In The Anti-Tank Role

In summary, when used in this way these guns, despite their physical disadvantages (whether towed or porteed), were again more effective than tanks. T = 13 compared to 8.4 for tank equivalence, but only just over half as effective as they were in the defence role. This surprising result must be mainly attributable to the higher proportion of more senior ranks (officers and SNCOs) involved with the *de facto* manning of guns than of tanks. The higher ranks had a higher probability of heroic action and, even in non-heroic cases, a separate extra benefit due to supervision can be deduced. This is also easier to apply to non-enclosed crews.

A major factor that has emerged from this part of the analysis is the significance of anti-tank guns in World War II anti-tank combat. In particular, it has been shown that in defence the anti-tank gun was more effective than the tank. This is not at all apparent from most historical accounts of combat, apart from those quoted and some which recognise the significance of certain German anti-tank guns.

* The 0.36 Factor represents the ratio of effectiveness at 0.20 heroes per gun, the mean incidence, to that at one hero /gun in these battles i.e. 0.24 + (0.2 x 0.8) = 0.36.

It appears, therefore, that a blurred perception of the general significance of tanks and their anti-tank capability has emerged. Although effective in other roles they are not necessarily the most effective anti-tank weapon in defence. As a result, it appears that some areas of military history would benefit from a re-evaluation which would focus in particular on the roles, disposition and numbers of anti-tank guns in actions as well as those of tanks (whose numbers are frequently recorded in isolation). Such an evaluation is necessary for an objective understanding of casualties in armoured combat, particularly in the Western Desert. The other side of the coin, but of equal importance, lies in understanding and quantifying the true benefits of tanks in combat roles other than in the anti-tank battle.

Whilst this chapter has introduced the importance of heroism, this phase of study only introduced us to the analysis of the armoured battle. In addition to the results illustrated it has been possible to make estimates of the effects of supervision and of zero participation. (The latter is included in the next chapter).

Completing the Cycle: Comparisons of Armoured Combat and Exercises up to 1975

The importance of the study of World War 2 armoured combat as a first step was in the relatively large homogeneous sample of battles for analysis. Having established relationships for those we could extend to the more fragmentary samples since 1945, particularly in the Arab-Israeli combat up to 1973. This enabled the effects of newer weapon technology, and later armour protection, to be estimated for both tanks and anti-tank weapons (and in particular for anti-tank guided weapons). Moreover, since the 1973 war was at a similar level of technology to the weapons represented in our 1975 Chinese Eye exercise it was possible to close the loop on analysis by comparing relationships for combat and trials to make further estimates of combat degradation. These agreed well with the estimate of effects of crewing from the World War 2 studies. Thus, there was now a basis for bringing the results forward for newer systems. The next stage was to examine heroism (and supervision) in more detail to apply and test for other weapon systems.

SOURCE NOTES

[1] Silver John (Argent, Lt Col J N L) *Target Tank* p172 New South Wales, Australia, 1957

[2] Rainier, Major P *Pipeline into Battle* page 67 Heinemann, London , 1944

[3] Silver John op cit page 188

[4] Roberts, Maj Gen G P B *From the Desert to the Baltic* page 103 Kimber, London, 1987

[5] Messenger, Charles *The Tunisian Campaign* p69 Ian Allan, Shepperton, 1982

[6] War Diary 131 Queens Inf Bde National Archives (Kew) WO 169/ 8943

[7] Griffith, P G *British Armoured Warfare in the Western Desert 1940-1943* in Harris J P & Toase F N ed *Armoured Warfare* p78 Batsford, London, 1990

[8] Lucas Phillips, C E *Victoria Cross Battles of the Second World War* p77 Heinemann, London, 1973 and *Alamein* p56 Heinemann, London, 1962

[9] The Development of Artillery Testing and Equipment, War Office 1951

[10] *Gunners: A Saga of Rhodesian Artillerymen* in Tort, Journal of the Southern Rhodesian Artillery Association, 1947

[11] *The Development of Artillery Testing and Equipment* op cit p75

[12] Bright J, *The History of the Northumberland Hussars Yeomanry 1924-1949*, Mawson Swan & Morgan Ltd, 1949

[13] *The Development of Artillery Testing and Equipment* op cit p75

[14] Silver John op cit p98

[15] Murphy, W E 2nd *New Zealand Divisional Artillery* Dept of Internal Affairs, Wellington NZ, 1966 p207

[16] *Notes from Theatres of War No 10: Cyrenaica and W Desert* p22 War Office, 1942 under reference 26/GS publication/1047.

[17] *The Development of Artillery Testing and Equipment* op cit

[18] *Notes from Theatres of War No1: Cyrenaica* p13 War Office, 1941

[19] Gudmundsson, Bruce ed *Inside the Afrika Korps: the Crusader Battles 1941-1942* p310, Greenhill, London, 1999

[20] Bright J op cit p151 (quoting London Gazette dated 15 October 1942)

CHAPTER SIX
Heroism and Combat Degradation

"History as written and read does not divulge the source of leadership. Hence its study often induces us to forget its potency"

Gen George S Patton Jr, *The Secret of Victory.*

Heroes had been principally identified in the anti-armour study through medal citations. Before going any further, it is worth discussing their validity as an analytical tool. Considered purely from the point of view of estimating the likely effects of combat degradation, it is not the system of gallantry awards which is important, but the pattern of behaviour that these awards reflect. Nevertheless, the awards are our best means of identifying this behaviour *post hoc*, and of linking it to other factors. For present purposes we need to be assured both that gallantry awards are useful and reliable measures of military performance, and that they reflect something fundamental and enduring about the way that men are likely to behave under fire, in order to extend beyond the examples of the detailed battles.

One qualification to these citations is that the recipient must be in a hazardous situation at the right time and observers must be present. But variation of opportunity is inherent in all tactical situations, even in field trials. In trials, for instance, it is commonly found that a weapon at the upper 15 percentile point will fire four times as many rounds as will a weapon at the lower 15 percentile point. The position taken in this study is that the variation of individual weapon contributions is likely to be due simply to differences in opportunities to engage. Then it can be shown, on the basis of battle records, that the stresses of war, coupled with the heroism/non-heroism factor, increase this variability very considerably.

It would not be appropriate here to try to explain the variations in behaviour which, at one extreme, may result in a gallantry award. However, if we are to allow for it in combat models we need to understand its variability, especially the degree to which effectiveness may be seriously degraded. Here the conclusion by Marshall, based on extensive post-combat interviews of US troops, that combat degradation arises in large part from effective non-participation by a significant proportion of those nominally involved (see Chapter 4), is particularly relevant. Indeed, it is in line with the evidence collected during the course of this study. Heroism is characterised by a willingness to participate actively in the battle whatever the circumstances and its opposite by a refusal, or inability, to do so. In this study we shall attempt to quantify both the incidence of heroic behaviour and, in comparative terms, the relative contribution of the remainder. Two examples, both linked with gallantry citations, point both to the direct importance of the presence of officers and senior ranks in combat or in their absence, to the zero gun effectiveness possible even with intact guns. During the second phase of el Alamein in October 1942:

> "Nearby there were three 6 pounders of the Sherwood Foresters, but the detachment had lost all its officers and the guns were unmanned. Sgt Trail of 34 Battery went over to them across 300 yards of bullet-swept ground and brought one of them single handed into action against the tanks."[1]

And, at much the same time, another citation reveals the lack of action by guns sited to engage:

> "Three enemy M13 tanks approached the OP [Observation Post] overrunning the infantry around it. Observing that none of our Anti-tank guns had opened fire Captain Fielding ran to the nearest gun whilst being shot at by machine guns from the tanks. He brought the gun into action and laying it himself succeeded in knocking out one tank and turning the other two back."[2]

Another example emerged amongst accounts of one of the Alamein heroic stands in July 1942. A gun sergeant foraging for ammunition on a knocked out gun had left an NCO and gunner to keep his gun firing. He was surprised to see both leave the gun and return to the gun quad whose driver drove them away. Although he shouted at them to stop and fired six shots with his revolver they disappeared and were not seen again.[3]

There may well be some physiological reasons why people act heroically, but all the evidence suggests that in the main it is a matter of genetics, social conditioning and values. We had identified different patterns of gallant behaviour in this study and several; anecdotal examples indicated associations which suggested that further investigation could enable us to follow the mechanism of unit effectiveness increasing with combat experience.

The Incidence of Heroism

The method of analysis now adopted is summarised below:

a. The quantification over a number of separate actions or battles of:

(1) Allied weapons.
(2) Enemy losses.
(3) Associated Allied gallantry awards.

b. The calculation of the apparent effectiveness of Allied weapons and enemy losses.

c. The computation of the degree of association and numerical relationship between the number of gallantry awards per weapon and weapon effectiveness.

We initially returned to World War 2 anti-tank weapons and the pooled plot of weapon effectiveness (T) against the number of gallantry awards per weapon is summarised for the different gun types in Figures 6.1 and 6.2. The data in the latter pertaining to anti-tank guns has been split into subsets "with" and "without" mines and by gun type. In addition to approximately 40 actions from the detailed battles studied at the beginning of the anti-armour HA phase and Greece they included 80 separate battles, varying from the overrunning of a brigade's field artillery down to small groups and even individual weapons. All groups showed generally similar patterns, but that with minefields displayed a (non-significant) trend to less variation in effectiveness with heroism.

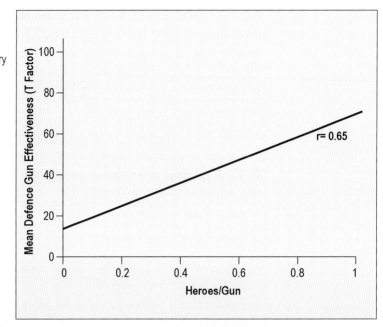

Figure 6.1
The Effect of Heroism on Defence Gun Effectiveness Summary of Results from Chapter 5

Figure 6.2
Summary of Defence Gun Effectiveness Variation with Heroism

	Defence Effectiveness (T)			
Data Set	At zero heros/gun	At one hero/gun	Ratio from 0 to one hero/gun	Sample
Anti-tank guns in Ground Role	14.0	100.5	7.14	25+20 (Survey + Detail)
Ground role with mines	32.1	61	1.90	19
Field Guns	13.5	68	5.00	35
Porteed Guns	14.6	64.4	4.40	25
Weighted Mean of all data			5.00	124

The factor of five, between heroes and others, confirms the results from detailed battle reconstructions. It is noticeable, too, that the approximate aggregated methods used in the broad survey result in slightly lower correlation coefficients than the more detailed examinations in the preliminary investigation. This is almost certainly because they cannot reflect the less than ideal allocation of heroes to guns in which one at least was part of each weapon's crew. Nevertheless, the association between heroism and combat effectiveness accounts for roughly one half of the variance of the latter.

It seems from the detailed analyses that, excluding those weapons manned by crews who received gallantry awards, approximately one third of weapons made no effective contribution to the battle at all. Their effectiveness was, to all intents and purposes, zero. The remaining two thirds operated at an effectiveness level of roughly 0.3. Consequently, at zero heroes per gun the expected combat effectiveness is: $(0.33 \times 0)+(0.67 \times 0.3)= 0.2$. From this a simple formula can be derived:

Expected combat performance* = 0.2 + (Heroes per gun) x 0.8

This equation holds up to a level of one hero per gun, which provides a combat performance of unity and is the same as that of peacetime trails. Above this level the effect of additional heroes is greatly reduced. It will also be noted from the aggregated analysis above that, even with zero heroes per gun, there is some residual combat effectiveness (estimated at 0.2 relative to the standard set by the heroes). It is necessary, however, to turn to the detailed analyses to gain additional insights as to the likely nature of the contribution from those not in receipt of gallantry awards.

Figure 6.3
Comparison of Three Levels of Effectiveness in Combat: Anti-Tank Study and Lt Col Wigram's Report on Infantry Platoon in Combat

Combat Participation by 'Non-Heroes'

This estimate of the proportions likely to contribute at different levels under fire ties in closely with the qualitative comments of Wigram on infantry platoon members in Sicily in 1943, which

Level	Wigram 1943 for Infantry Platoons		This Anti-Tank Study WWII A/Tk Guns	
	Proportion	Level	Proportion	Level
Most Effective	0.25	'Gutful'	0.18 (0.15-0.2)	1.0
Partly Effective	0.52	'Sheep'	0.55	0.3
Zero Effective	0.22	'Will Run Away'	0.27	0

* The effectiveness is relative to that which may be expected in peacetime trials.

THE STRESS OF BATTLE

were cited in Chapter Three. The likely incidence of heroism will be dealt with in the subsection below, but, anticipating those results, our own findings are compared with Wigram's comments in Figure 6.3.

These variations in effectiveness must now be linked to variations in the weapon system contribution arising simply from differences in opportunity to engage. It has already been mentioned that in field trials it is commonly found that a weapon at the upper 15 percentile point will fire four times as many rounds as will a weapon at the lower 15 percentile point. Put in statistical terms, the firing contribution of different weapons follows a log normal distribution, with a standard deviation equivalent to a ratio of 2. This finding holds good for anti-armour weapons and also for small arms in open, urban and even house clearance situations. Moreover, the effect changes little if measured from replicated battles on the same ground, or from a series of battles fought over fresh ground on each occasion.

For the purpose of separating the total variation in battle contribution into different components, the data from the detailed analyses has been divided into three groups: 'most effective', or heroes; the 'partly effective', or degraded; and the 'zero effective' group, who apparently did not participate at all. The effectiveness for the first two groups was computed in terms of the T index described above. The cumulative distribution of effectiveness indices for these two subsets is plotted in Figure 6.4 (It is, of course, impossible to plot a zero effectiveness group on a logarithmic scale). The important point to note here is that the slopes of the two lines through these two sets of data points both equate very nearly to a standard deviation representing a ratio of 2. This is the value obtained for variations in weapon performance in tactical trials of a range of situations, that is the variation due to weapon deployments as the forces meet. The conclusion must be that within each of the two groups, heroes and participating non-heroes, the variation in opportunities to engage approximates very closely to what might be expected from field trials. However, the heroism/non-heroism combination increases the total variability in

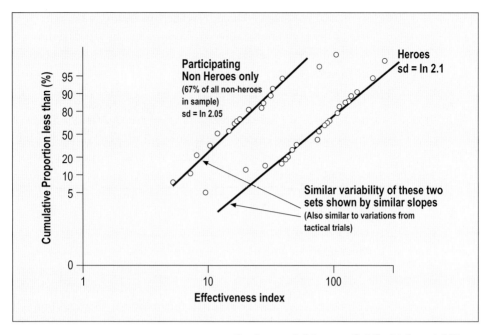

Figure 6.4
Pooled T Factor
Distributions from
Detailed Actions for
Heroes and Non-Heroes
(Medenine, Snipe and
Greece)

weapon system contribution and this superficially high variability is to be expected purely from this source, especially when the presence of the other extreme of the non-contributors are taken into account.

Returning to the heroes, the consistency of exceptional performance from those recognised for gallantry is a feature which emerges from regimental histories. Many cases are difficult to compare as gallantry can be manifested in many ways; and also many noted for gallantry subsequently received promotion so their responsibilities changed. Continuing gallantry has sometimes been recognised by further awards but, in general, it has required a more obvious act of gallantry, which is very evident from the comments designed to moderate citations so as to ensure that they were of a consistent standard. Examples of bars to awards of the MC and the DSO are infrequent, and there have only been three cases of bars to the VC. Records of bars recommended, compared with those awarded, indicates that a second award at any level requires a stronger case than does the first award.

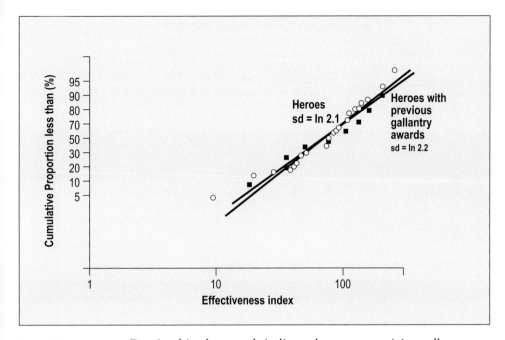

Figure 6.5
Pooled T Factor
Distributions for
Past Heroes

Despite this, the records indicate that many receiving gallantry awards had previously obtained a mention in dispatches and there is also a significant group of multi-award winners testifying to continuing gallant performance. In addition, the same names often recur in unit histories for successive specific actions. A further comparison was therefore made, building up a sample of anti-tank guns manned by 'heroes' identified by awards in previous battles. From our anti-tank study it was possible to make a more quantifiable check on the subsequent performance of gallantry award winners, where those with previous awards take part in further actions which we had already quantified. A sample of nine such plotted in Figure 6.5 above shows a close approximation to that of the overall heroic set in Figure 6.4. The geometric mean 59 compares to 65 for the identified heroes of Medenine, Snipe and Greece 1941. The standard ratio of the group approximates 2.2 for previous heroes compared to 2.1 for newly recognised heroes.

The overall conclusion is that heroes, even without further awards, maintain their combat performance, but do not increase it.

The Association of Heroic Action with Rank

Figure 6.6
Probability of Heroic
Action by Rank Groups
(as % of Those
Estimated to be
Available for Manning)

From the detailed surveys, it was also possible to estimate the proportions of the officers, SNCOs and ORs associated with these World War 2 anti-tank guns who received gallantry awards. The figures are:

Gun		Sample	Rank		
Type		Sample	Officers	SNCOs*	NCOs and OR
Anti-Tank Guns	2pdr/37mm	521	10	5.1	1.3
	6 pdr	387	16	13	1.9
Field Guns	18/25 pdr*	465	15	7.1	1.2
Pooled (incl misc guns)		1435	14	8.4	1.3
Ratio Officers:SNCOs:ORs			1.0	0.6	0.09

The pooled results indicate value aggregated from the three rows above plus minor cases (not detailed) including 17 pdr anti-tank and medium guns, as well as the Bofors LAA gun.

In order to accept these as Army-wide estimates of the potential for heroic acts among the different ranks it was necessary to be assured that the proportions were not likely to differ very greatly in other groups. In Figure 6.7 the results of a separate comparison based on a number of regimental histories of different arms are shown. These give the ratio of awards to numbers killed in action (so that the exposure to risk is roughly equated) throughout the whole of World War 2. Taken overall, in regiments the overall ratio of officers: SNCOs: ORs is strikingly similar to that in Figure 6.6 opposite. It can be tentatively concluded that the association between rank and heroism is likely to be similar in armoured regiments to that already discovered in the infantry and artillery sample.

* The 18 pdr field gun, the staple of the Royal Field Artillery in World War 1, had been obsolete since the introduction of the 25 pdr in 1940, but was found a temporary new role as an anti-tank gun to complement the 2pdr until the issue of the new 6 pdr anti-tank gun in 1942.

Unit Type (Sample)	Awards/KIA Ratio (Geometric Means)		
	Officers	SNCO's (Sgt +)	OR
Armoured Regts [10]	1.73	1.06	0.13
Armoured Car Regts [5]	2.32	1.13	0.10
Infantry Regts [30 bns from 9 regts]	1.03	0.57	0.06
Fd Artillery Regts [8]	1.90	0.70	0.13
A/Tk Regts [2]	1.25	0.67	0.08
Overall	1.56	0.81	0.10
Ratio of Officers:SNCOs:ORs	1.00	0.52	0.06
Fig 6.6 Ratio of Officers:SNCOs:ORs	1.00	0.60	0.09

Figure 6.7
Comparison of Gallantry Awards: Killed in Action Ratios by Rank and Arm (WWII) (Sample of Units)

The analyses of anti-tank combat based initially on detailed reconstructions, with confirmation from wider if less detailed samples, have provided the beginning of an understanding of the variations in individual behaviour which, together, make up aggregate combat performance and hence, by comparison with the best, combat degradation. The incidence of observed heroic behaviour has been shown to vary with rank for anti-tank and artillery crews. This is also reflected in the independent measurement across other arms as well; the measurement (gallantry awards/KIA) for a unit provides a measure of incidence scaled in ratio of risk (KIA at that rank).

The next stage was to examine the incidence of awards within the three broad rank bands, concentrating in particular on the variation between junior NCOs (full Corporal and below) and private soldiers. This analysis uses the same pooled sample of 1,435 anti-tank gun deployments as in Figure 6.6, with total estimated crewing (including supervision by non-designated crew members) based on known manning from a sample of deployments for each gun type. The officer manning has not been further split by rank for this assessment, as the officers present will all be *de facto* additions to the gun crew present, hence prompting a biased sub-set in comparison, say, with junior officer infantry platoon commanders.

Rank/Group	Total Awards to Rank	Total Manning Deployed Guns	Probabilities of recognised heroic action
Officers	134	982	14%
SNCOs	124	1473	8.4%
JNCOs	49	1661	2.95%
Privates	32	4409	0.73%

Figure 6.8
Analysis of Gallantry Award by Rank for all Guns in Direct Fire Anti-tank Role

The effect of this analysis is to replace an estimate of 1.3% of heroism, for all ranks below sergeant, by two estimates, of approximately 3% for junior NCOs and less than 1% for privates and equivalent. The hypothesised pattern of general increase in the likelihood of an award being governed by rank, rather than of three levels of incidence (as in the initial analysis), is strengthened.

Comparison Between Arms

Fig 6.9
Rifle Brigade: Awards and Fatal Casualties

We then analysed 53 British World War 2 infantry battalions in much the same way, building on those in Figure 6.7. Unlike the anti-tank gun study, it was possible to divide the officers band into Captains and above (within a battalion) and subalterns (Lts, 2Lts).

	Total Awards to Rank	Total KIA & DOW	Gallantry Awards per man killed	Relative to all Officers in Bn	Probability of recognisable Heroic action
a	b	c	d	e	f
Senior Officers	91	45	2.02	2.04	29%
Lieutenants	63	111	0.57	0.57	8%
All Officers	154	156	0.99	1.00	14%
Sgts (all levels)	70	113	0.62	0.63	8.8%
Corporal L/Corporals and equivalents	44	187	0.235	0.24	3.4%
Privates and equivalents	32	845	0.038	0.038	0.53%

THE STRESS OF BATTLE

Derived data and extra detail from the original sources was tabulated for each battalion considered. The summarised award data was combined with casualty data. In each case the awards/fatal casualty ratios were compared to the figure for all officers of the unit(s). These were then used to estimate the incidence of heroic behaviour, based on the 14% estimate for all officers in the anti-gun study.

Figure 6.10
Estimate of Incidence of Heroism by Rank Group from Infantry Battalion Data

To follow the process consider the data in Figure 6.9from the six battalions of the Rifle Brigade in World War 2.

Column d is simply the ratio of Column b to Column c, while Column e uses the column d figures scaling all by the ratio

Rank Group	Awards per Fatal Casualty (compared to all Officers of Regiment)		Estimated incidence of recognised heroic behaviour (based on 14% mean for all officers)
	Geo mean	Std. Ratio	
Senior Officers (in regiment)	2.11	1.54	30%
Lieutenants	0.435	1.63	6.1%
Warrant Officers and Sergeants	0.435	1.55	6.1%
Corporals and Lance-Corporals (and equivalent)	0.18	1.87	2.5%
Privates (and equivalents)	0.034	1.81	0.48%

necessary to change the "all officers" line to 1.0, ie a ratio of 1.01). The best estimate for probability of gallantry from all officers (see Figure 6.8) is 14%, hence scaling the others in the ratios of Column e provides an estimation of the equivalent of probabilities for other ranks in Column f.

Taking the (geometric) mean of the data for all 53 battalions, the improved estimate shown in Figure 6.10 was obtained:

Figure 6.11
Estimated Incidence of Recognised Heroic Behaviour for Infantry Combat

Ranks	For Infantry (from awards/kill, by comparison with all officers at 14%)	Confirmation from independent data for anti-tank gun crews (Inf and Arty) (Fig 6.8)
Lieutenants	6.1%	-
Sergeants (all levels)	6.1%	8.4%
Corporals/ Lance-corporals and equivalent	2.5%	2.9%
Privates and equivalent	0.48%	0.73%

The two sets of results in Figures 6.8 and 6.10 may now be compared in Figure 6.11. On this finer grading by rank, as in the initial analysis, the two methods agree well. The indirect estimate is considered the more appropriate for infantry platoon combat, the anti-tank data providing broad confirmation.

An independent comparison is also possible for the distinct data sets of artillery in 1st Airborne Division at Arnhem in September 1944. A detailed study collected together sufficient data for analysis by the two methods used above. The comparison of estimates by both methods is tabulated in Figure 6.12 below.

Figure 6.12
Comparison of Two Assessment Methods for Estimation of Heroic Behaviour for Artillery at Arnhem

	Estimation by	
Ranks	Awards and No. of Guns Deployed	Awards and Fatal Casualties
Senior Officers	30%	34%
Lieutenants*	13%	4.2%
All Officers	23%	14%
Sergeants	9%	8.4%
JNCOs	3.8%	2.8%
Privates	0.9%	0.73%

* Only 16 estimated in sample with two gallantry awards, if only one had occurred 13% would become 6%.

Again, the data for non-commissioned ranks correlates well, but for 'all officers' and especially the very small sample for Lieutenants,* the agreement is not so good. The overall probabilities are slightly higher than the anti-tank analysis for North Africa, but of similar order. However, the relative numbers of awards to each rank group are not significantly different by chi-squared test** between the two methods (whether considered by each rank in the table or pooled because of paucity of numbers). Furthermore, apart from providing an independent comparison with the previous analyses, and showing that both methods provide similar estimates, this data set has a fundamental difference from that used in the previous analysis in that the two methods cover the same force for the same period. It is in this context that the Figure 6.12 results should be compared with those in Figures 6.8 and 6.10.

As for post-1945 awards, we did make a simple comparison of British and Gurkha battalions in the period 1947-1982 with equivalent units in World War 2. This indicated that the ratios of Awards/KIA has been higher in the later non-World War environment, with the post-war ratio averaging 3.4 times higher. As yet, we have not established why this should be so, although several hypotheses are possible.

Comparison with the Israeli Army's Recognition of Heroism by Rank

There remained a possible doubt that this award pattern could be a peculiarity of the British Army. A comparison was therefore made with the Israeli Army in the 1973 Yom Kippur War. In all, apart from eight at the highest award level (the Ott Hagvurah), which constituted a very small and exceptional group, 291 medals were awarded to the Israeli Defence Forces. Their distribution was as in Figure 6.13.

Unfortunately, it proved impossible to establish the equivalent KIA figures by rank, but an estimate can be made, using the total

** The chi-squared test is used to test the goodness of fit of the theoretical distribution (or one independently derived) and observed data.
It measures the extent to which the observed proportions differ from those which would be expected purely by chance.

Figure 6.13
Israeli Medal Recipients
by Rank, Yom Kippur
War

Rank	No	% of Total
Senior Officer (Major to Colonel)	75	26.5
Junior Officer (2nd Lt to Captain)	106	37.4
Senior NCO (Sgt to RSM)	67	23.7
Junior Ranks (Private to Corporal)	35	12.4
	283	100

Figure 6.14
Estimated distribution
of Award/KIA to Israeli
forces in Yom Kippur
War

Israeli KIA casualties in 1973, and the distribution of Israeli casualties by rank from the 1982 war in Lebanon:

Rank	Gallantry Awards	Estimated KIA	Award/KIA (%)
Senior Officer (Major to Colonel)	75	81	93
Junior Officer (2nd Lt to Captain)	106	344	31
Senior NCO (Sgt to RSM)	67	471(+)*	14(-)
Junior Ranks (Private to Corporal)	35	1794(-)*	2(+)
	283	2690	(10.5)

The overall pattern of this ratio with rank group is clearly similar to that of the British World War 2 level awards, despite some uncertainty on the SNCO and Junior Rank relative values. The overall levels are approximately two to three times higher than the British by rank but since the criteria for the various awards were different from those of the British, no deductions on effectiveness can be made. However, the ratios by rank can be correlated with the British figures as below (Figure 6.15). This uses four British sets - British infantry World War 2 and post-war, British gunners at Arnhem by the two alternative measures.

The comparison points to very similar variations with rank (by a power of 1.1), although a significantly higher apparent incidence for heroism by Israelis. Whether this is a rank difference or one in the threshold for awards can only be determined by comparing combat effectiveness as in the example opposite.

* These two figures for KIA are distorted by the inclusion of casualties to junior sergeants with those of corporals and lower ranks. Hence the SNCO to lower rank difference on awards/KIA is imprecise, as indicated by the (+) and (-) sign.

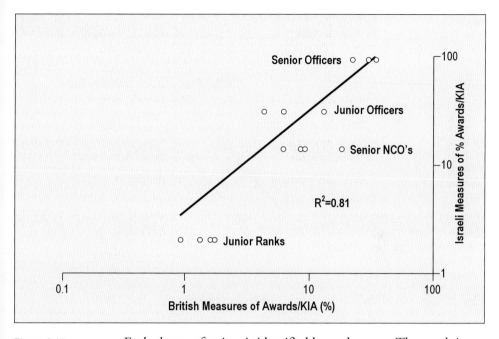

Figure 6.15
Correlation of British and Israeli Measures of Awards /KIA by Rank Group

Each cluster of points is identified by rank group. The graph is plotted on a log-log basis because the wide and increasing spacing between values of awards/KIA would otherwise mean that correlation would be exaggerated by the high values of the senior officers group. The high correlation of R = 0.9 means that the observed variation of Israeli awards by rank given by R^2 is 0.81 or 81% explained by the British model of variation by rank.

Comparison of Gurkha Defence Effectiveness and Gallantry Awards

Another combat effectiveness comparison is possible between units of the British Army. Gurkha regiments have similar rank structure to British Infantry regiments and, below commissioned officer level, have been entirely Gurkha manned. In his foreword to Brigadier Bredin's book *The Happy Warriors*,[4] Field Marshal Lord Harding, who was Colonel-in-Chief of the 6th Gurkhas, while disclaiming any direct family association with the Gurkhas or of commanding or serving in a Gurkha unit stated that "I have had experience of their skill and prowess, their courage and endurance on many different battlefields". Bredin himself had been inspired to write the book by two years as Commanding

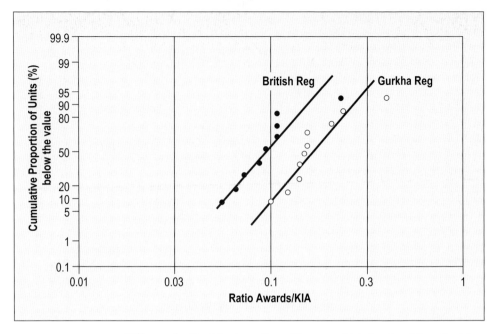

Figure 6.16
Comparison of Gallantry
Awards for British and
Gurkha Regiments

Officer of a Gurkha battalion. He started his book with a Gurkha comment during the siege of Bhurtpore in 1825: "The English are as brave as lions; they are splendid sepoys, and are very nearly equal to us."

The Canadian anthropologist, Lionel Caplan[5] took a different view. His thesis is that "the overwhelming tendency is to represent them as invincible, 'the bravest of the brave', a phrase which occurs in the Preface of Turner's splendid Nepali dictionary and is quoted in many subsequent writings… "The romance becomes reality through repetition and publication…" Whilst acknowledging their many gallantry awards, the thrust of his work is that a large part of their reputation has nevertheless been built on Western perception. With the many favourable military opinions, often emotive from their British officers, and Caplan's contrasting disbelieving view, it is possible to find an objective comparison through historical analysis.

If the appropriate pooled figures (for SNCOs and all other ranks) are compared with the British equivalents, they show a significantly higher incidence of gallantry by 1.6 times, as illustrated in Figure 6.16.

THE STRESS OF BATTLE

Criterion	British Infantry	Gurkha Infantry	Ratio British to Gurkha
Defensive Infantry combat WWI to WWII (attack cas / defender at 1:1 in open country)	0.23	0.37	1:1.62
Casualty infliction on insurgent guerrilla forces in Malaya (53-54) as Kills per Contact & Bn eliminations per year	0.63 & 0.65 22.8 & 16.0	1.0 & 1.02 32.7 & 28.1	1:1.59 1:1.59
Gallantry Awards per KIA in WWII (exc. officers)	0.105	0.168	1:1.60

Figure 6.17
Comparisons of British and Gurkha Infantry

While these results certainly confirm the Gurkha reputation for bravery, they are no measure of combat effectiveness *per se*. Consequently, we compared British and Gurkha ability in inflict casualties, using sets of defensive actions from World Wars 1 and 2, as well annual reports on unit effectiveness in 1953-54 during the Malayan Emergency:[6]

It will be seen that the ratios of British/Gurkha performance are remarkably similar to that for gallantry awards and help to confirm the close relationship between awards and combat effectiveness. They also serve to disprove the Caplan thesis that the Gurkhas are no more effective than other troops. A similar but preliminary comparison between British infantry and a group of elite units also shows increases in effectiveness and similar increases in gallantry awards per KIA; however this has not yet been taken far enough to give significant differences in either.

Further Study of Non-Heroic Performance

Returning to the non-heroic groups, it was mentioned in the previous chapter that the detailed reconstructions of armour/anti-armour battles identified cases where it was clear that weapons with crews available had not engaged enemy vehicles within range although others were engaging them. This sub-group could be clearly identified in each of the groups of battles studied in detail. Conservative estimates of these are summarised in the table below;

they are deliberately conservative being the cases where it could be cautiously assessed from positional and historical data that the opportunity to engage had occurred and not been taken. In many

Figure 6.18
Non heroically manned guns at zero effectiveness

	Total non-heroically manned guns	Total guns at zero effectiveness
Anti-tank battles in Greece	44	9
Anti-tank battles in SNIPE (Alamein)	27	12
Anti-tank battles at Medenine	49	20
Total	120	41

others, it was accepted that they *may* have seen enemy within range, but they were excluded because this could not be established with any degree of confidence.

Hence the total from pooling these sets is 41 of 120 non-heroically manned guns at zero effectiveness or 34% of such gun crews or, since these non-heroically manned guns were only approx. 80% of the total, 34 x 0.8 = 27% of all crews as in Figure 6.3.

Another method of estimation can be applied more generally. It is, however, not conservative but applicable to cases where any contribution is expected to cause some vehicle loss. Estimation of probability of zero individual contribution from those non-heroic defences where the total overall gun effectiveness is zero is also a possibility. This depends on assigning a probability 'p' of zero effectiveness to any non heroic gun crew. * Then for a battle with 'n' guns available in defence the probability of zero overall performance (when all are at zero) is p^n. Given the varying numbers of guns/battle in different sizes we need to look at all battles with non heroic defence and estimate the total, from all sizes of zero effectiveness.

---

* This 'p' actually represents the combination of the probability of not participating and the probability of any participation being non-lethal. Hence the value of 'p' assessed by this method will be higher than that simply from observed non-partricipation.

The data in Figure 6.19 shows those battles in our sample which had all non-heroically manned guns (excluding those used from detailed assessment in Figure 6.18). Of these 22 battles, five showed zero gun effectiveness overall. However, two of those five included

Figure 6.19
Battles with All Non-Heroically Manned Guns

Analysis Group	Theatre of War	Number of Guns	Zero Total Gun Effectiveness
Anti-Tank gun static	GR	2	√
	TUN	6	√* (see footnote)
	TUN	1	√
	NA	2	-
	NA	24	-
	NA	4	-
Anti-Tank gun static with Mines	NA	25	-
	NA	1	-
	NA	18	-
Portee	NA	6	√* (see footnote)
	GR	3	-
	GR	3	-
	NA	16	-
	NA	17	-
	NA	3	-
Field Artillery in anti-tank role	GR	2	-
	GR	2	√
	GR	4	-
	GR	3	-
	NA	32	-
	NA	8	-
	NA	4	-

GR = Greece 1941, NA = North Africa (Egypt/Cyrenaica 1941-1942), TUN = Tunisia 1942-1943

total gun contributions which were arrived at by deducting the estimated casualties due to tanks. Hence, they are not reliable zero estimates and are better discarded.

* Zero total arrived at by deducting estimated casualties due to tanks (at mean effectiveness) from total, thus this is not a reliable zero assessment.

From the total guns available in each and the pn expression, the expected number of battles showing zero gun effectiveness can be estimated for any given value of p. For example, if p=0.5, then the expected proportion of

1-gun battles at zero	= 0.5,
2-gun battles at zero	= 0.25,
3-gun battles at zero	= 0.125 and so on.

As there are two 1-gun battles, four 2-gun battles, four 3-gun battles etc, in the samples the expected number of zeros will be:

$(0.5 \times 2) + (0.25 \times 4) + (0.125 \times 4) + \cdots$, including all battle sizes.
= 2.73 total battles at zero

This calculation yields the following:

		1.	
P=	0.4	expected zero total for all guns	For 1.80 battles
	0.5	expected zero total for all guns	For 2.73 battles
	0.6	expected zero total for all guns	For 4.0 battles
	0.7	expected zero total for all guns	For 5.7 battles

These can be compared to the three battles found (conservatively) to be at zero, indicating an estimated number of p in the range 0.5 to 0.6 or 50-60%. Clearly with this sample of battles and these values, this is not a sensitive determination but it does indicate a higher value than the 34% derived from the detailed histories of battles, partly for the reason given in the footnote on the previous page. Both of these figures relate to proportions of non heroically manned guns and if converted to a proportion of total guns they will be 0.27 and 0.4 to 0.48.

Similar assessments have also been made for groups of tank versus tank battles and for a set of US self-propelled M10 tank destroyers in NW Europe 1944-45 and Italy 1944. Based on the same method as above, the tank destroyers, with their guns in turrets, tank-like mobility and individual vehicle radios, indicated 55% of non-heroically manned weapons at zero effectiveness, very similar

THE STRESS OF BATTLE

to the towed guns. Using the same method again, the proportion for tanks has been estimated at 90-94% of non-heroically manned World War 2 tank battles in North Africa.

Thus, after allowing for the estimated 9% of tanks heroically manned, the proportion of all tanks estimated at zero can be estimated as 0.91 x 90-94%= 82-85%. Whilst this figure does appear high, the caveat in the preceding page footnote also applies in that it will be higher than directly observed non-participation since it includes non-lethal and non-damaging fire. There have as yet been no detailed studies from which to derive a conservative direct estimate of observed non-participation figures comparable to the 34% anti-tank gun figures. Yet, given the lower mean effectiveness in tank killing by tanks, which has been calculated independently of the data for non-participation, the 82-85% for tanks is comparable to the 40-48% for anti-tank guns and the similar figure for SP anti-tank guns.

The graphs in Figure 6.20 indicate some of these effects and the relationship with heroes/guns. That for guns is based on the pooled empirical anti-tank gun results and also shows the estimated mean level of heroes for guns and the corresponding mean effectiveness of 42%. The equivalent line for tanks is estimated based on the mean heroism and mean effectiveness at one hero/tank and the linear relationship corresponding to the expressed one for guns. The lower range of the other graph, up to 0:3 heroes/guns on tanks, illustrates the higher gun intercept at zero heroism, so much so that it also exceeds the mean tank effectiveness (at average heroism).

In the detailed studies of anti-tank combat there are examples of the beneficial effects of supervision in combat by undecorated officers and SNCOs. More generally the plots of effectiveness against mean heroes/weapon (Figure 5.10) indicate that even at zero heroism the effectiveness of anti-tank guns was higher than that of the average of tanks (with equivalent weapons) including the latter's mean level of heroes. As has been stated earlier, the suspicion is that the lower ratio of officers and SNCOs per weapon with tanks is the reason. A simple model was derived on this

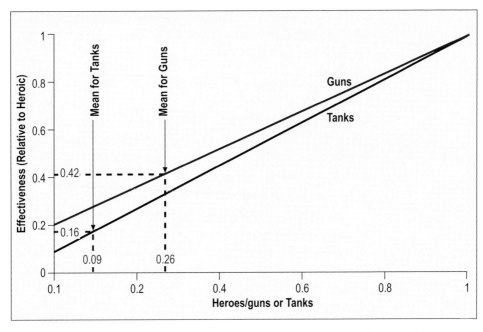

Figure 6.20
Comparison of gun and tank effectiveness (in tank killing) illustrating effect of heroism

hypothetical basis and calibrated for tanks and anti-tank guns. It revealed that the effect of non-heroic supervision was an increase of some 10 per cent effectiveness per supervisor per weapon.

A later modelling approach calibrated a wider sample of situations, including infantry weapons. This explored the effect of a hypothetical increase in weapon effectiveness to the level of that of the highest participating member of a crew (heroic, degraded or zero). It also included estimating the proportions of each rank group acting at participation other than at the heroic or zero levels. Examination of alternatives indicated that the simplest hypothesis, that the participation of every member of the team was raised to the level of the team member with highest participation, gave the best fit. However, this also implied that the proportion of officers and SNCOs at partial participation, without supervision, was fairly small.

An associated aspect examined was whether remote supervision by radio would improve levels of participation, apart from the other benefits of radio communications. It was found not to do so, leadership in person apparently being the important aspect. This aspect of non-heroic supervision remains for the present only partially solved, with more detailed empirical data needed to make a useful advance.

Wider Comparisons

Apart from the heroic minority, the remainder of those in combat appeared to behave as either of two subgroups - a majority of anti-tank weapon crews, at least, display degraded performance at approximately one third the heroic level from anti-tank weapon assessment, while the remainder perform at zero effectiveness. To establish whether this was unique to military combat or merely a reflection of the human character, we compared the assessments to others in non-military threat situations. These ranged from timidity in babies to adult behaviour in disaster situations.

In 1994, Jerome Kagan, a developmental psychologist at Harvard University investigated the inborn variation between babies, which included an assessment that 20% of babies have 'timid' temperaments. That is they react adversely to strange moving objects or voices and, at 4 years, will "balk and turn to their mothers when a psychologist orders the tot do something 'naughty'". Conversely, "at the other end of the spectrum, 35% of children take these events in their stride".[7] Dr J Leach a survival psychologist at Lancaster University attempted to determine what distinguishes the survivors and victims in disaster situations. He estimated that, overall: "…15% of individuals keep a cool head in a disaster and devise an escape plan; 75 % cannot decide between courses of action and seek further information; and 10% suffer from 'cognitive dysfunction'."[8] He also observed that for some, personal survival was the overriding consideration. Caution is therefore needed in correlating a strong survival instinct with gallantry. In disasters, there will be those whose actions are wholly selfish whilst, conversely, some of the 'wait for instruction' category, once stimulated into activity, may act with courage and a selfless regard for others.

We compared these two findings to the Marshall and Wigram observations and our own anti-tank gun study:

Behaviour	Kagan for Babies	Marshall Post Combat Interviews	Wigram Combat Observation	Historical Analysis of Combat	Leach Disaster Behaviour[4]
				Anti-Tank Gun Crews	
Brave	35	15	25	18	15
Intermediate	45	} 85	{ 50-59	55	75
Timid	20		{ 16-25	27	10

Figure 6.21
Comparison of Division of Individual Behaviour in Crises (Figures in %)

Although the one classification of babies is not identical to the two combat classifications, it is similar in that all show broadly the same proportions, as well as indicating a three-way division, although Marshall did not subdivide the Intermediate and Timid categories. It is, however, worth remarking that Wigram's three-way division was supported by other officers in 78th Division, in which Wigram eventually served. Colonel Grazebrook, a battalion commander, wrote that "the average platoon includes three or four heroes, three or four irreconcilables and the rest respond in direct relationship to the quality of their leaders".[9] Similarly, Brigadier Russell MC, commander of 38 Irish Brigade, observed that "a platoon is not made of 30 odd fearless heroes but of about half a dozen really good men, fifteen or so "sheep" and the remainder would often as not "lie dogo" or even retire but for the effort of junior officers and NCOs."[10] Whilst each imparts a slightly different perspective, all three explicitly agree on the three-way division. Moreover, after the end of the war General Sir Brian Horrocks was expounding a similar division: "In a section of ten man as a rough guide, two lead, seven follow and one would do about anything not to be there at all."[11]

The analysis described above has related to three levels: heroic, degraded and zero effectiveness in combat. For British forces all gallantry awards above a Mention in Despatches were included together. It may possibly be, however, that the very highest awards – the British Victoria Cross, US Congressional Medal of Honor, and Israeli Ott Hagvurah, for example – could represent a fourth level of 'super hero' in that they specify that the act of bravery must be a high risk to the individual's life. While this level would be small in numbers the even higher combat performance represented would serve to degrade that at the lower levels of performance.

Summing Up the Variations in Combat Performance

To summarise this chapter, while the study of infantry behaviour in combat established an estimate of an overall degradation factor, the investigation of armour/anti-armour combat was able to separate some of the elements of the processes leading to such degradation. The key factors established were:

a. The participation of weapons crews and individuals in combat could be separated as three levels rather than a continuum. For simplicity, these are termed hero, degraded and zero. Whether these have a part hereditary or genetic origin has not yet been established, although some work has been done on the family trees of individuals of recognised gallantry in an effort to establish a basis for testing.

b. Study of heroic behaviour has shown that the probability varied with rank, although to what extent this was cause (being promoted because of heroic behaviour) and effects (of the responsibility of higher rank) is not yet clear. Heroic behaviour has also been shown to be recurring by the same individuals, given the appropriate opportunity.

c. The anti-tank and other gun crews studied operated at a level of effectiveness characterised by the highest level of those in the de facto crew, which could include officers and SNCOs in the same unit or even those in the same area. In some cases this was done by one (or more) heroic individuals fulfilling the crew roles, in others it was due to the crew following the leadership of the heroic participant.

d. An additional mechanism identified for non-heroic crews was that of supervision which, even when by those not recognised as heroic, also acted to give higher mean crew effectiveness. The lower supervision and the lower rank mix of tank crews appeared to be the cause of their lower tank killing effectiveness compared to gun crews with equivalent weapons.

e. Estimation of the proportion of crews (or men) at zero effectiveness, whilst able to engage targets, is difficult. Such estimates that have been made have either been through detailed reconstruction, which gives conservative figures, or by looking at battles with few casualties on one side or both. This approach appears to give estimates that are higher than actual.

f. Overall effectiveness in combat, as a proportion of that physically possible, has been estimated as a proportion of the heroic crews' mean level.

Whilst this chapter has delved further into the mechanism of a basic combat degradation there can be other factors leading to further reductions of performance. Suppression by bombardment was explored for infantry in an earlier chapter and has been confirmed for anti-tank crews. However, the additional effects of surprise and shock have long been employed by the military with the intention of gaining an advantage over opponents. In the following chapter we explore the extent to which these effects can be measured.

SOURCE NOTES

[1] Murphy, W E *2nd New Zealand Divisional Artillery* pp407-8 Dept of Internal Affairs, Wellington, 1966

[2] National Archives, Kew WO 373/24

[3] Author's interview with an eyewitness in 1993

[4] Published by the Blackmore Press, Gillingham, Dorset,1961

[5] In *Warrior Gentlemen* Berghahn Books, Oxford, 1995

[6] These are given in Coates, J *Suppressing Insurgency* Westview Press, Colorado, 1992

[7] *New Scientist* 26 February 1994

[8] Channel Four TV Equinox documentary *Alive* screened on 6 October 1996

[9] Grazebrook Col T.N. *Notes on Questionnaires* National Archives, Kew WO 231/14

[10] Russell, Brig M MC *Report to 78 Div: Lessons of the Sicily Campaign* Ibid, WO 204/8275

[11] Horrocks Lt Gen Sir B *A Full Life* p166 Collins, London, 1960

CHAPTER SEVEN
Historical Analysis of Surprise and Shock Effects

Following the historical analysis of combat degradation generally and of its variations due to suppressive fire, we were asked to assess further variations due to the effects of shock and surprise and to investigate the causes of these phenomena. Although linkage between the two was suspected and they have often been mentioned together, we examined them separately in order to gain a better understanding.

Surprise

We defined Surprise as:

> "The achievement of the unexpected in timing, place or direction of an initiative covering an Attack or Counter-Attack, but not excluding the Defence's ability to surprise, for example by deployment or control of fire. It can also include the effect of Surprise by weapon type, their combined use, strength, numbers or speed."

Surprise occurs when an act or development has taken place contrary to expectations, thus proving previous assumptions to be ill founded. The response to a Surprise Attack is normally inadequate and the attack itself may produce an "emotional" effect that reduces the ability to respond in the short term. The degree of surprise achieved is dependent not only on the victim's mistaken assumptions, but also on his lack of advance warning of the attack, and his lack of preparation to deal with the unexpected. Indeed, the basis of Surprise is to catch the enemy unawares, so that he cannot react properly, the emphasis being on the word 'cannot'. The effect is to deny the victim the time and space in which to give the necessary orders for the troops to react, for meaningful firepower to be deployed, and for timely countermoves to be made. In summary, the overall effect of Surprise is that soldiers cannot perform, while that of Shock is that soldiers could have but didn't.

The effects were examined by historical analysis at both tactical and operational levels, but for the purposes of the combat degradation study we will consider only the tactical level. Suffice to say that the effects of the higher level surprise, which could, of course, occur in parallel with lower, tactical level surprise, were assessed as being much greater than those at the lower level.

The battles previously studied for assessment of defence effectiveness were revisited for an historian's assessment from the battle descriptions of whether surprise was achieved. At the same time, the achievement of defence shock was also assessed from these accounts. Within the broad categories outlined above there were constraints on the actions that could be considered because of the type of data required. The actions considered had to be those that primarily involved infantry versus infantry combat in open country and without counter-attack. This was so that the effect of shock in defence could be assessed separately from the that on the attackers during the counter-attack phase, something not possible for more complicated battles. The resolution of data required in this work was such that for the actions under consideration the numbers and types and losses of men and equipments on each side needed to be known. The data was drawn from unit war diaries, regimental, campaign and official histories, and personal recollections.

Surprise in Infantry Combat

Using the data from the actions and the methodology developed for infantry combat in Chapter 3, the casualties caused per machine gun equivalent for each action were found by correcting for the effects of the other factors, namely tanks, attack artillery, fortifications and force ratio. Casualties caused by the combined effect of defensive machine guns and rifles were calculated after allowing for the casualties due to defensive mortars and artillery as described above. The use of this methodology depends on various assumptions about the organisations of units and their methods of operation and particularly on the interpretation of what actually happened on the ground. The historical records are at times scanty, and thus it was important to be consistent in the application of the

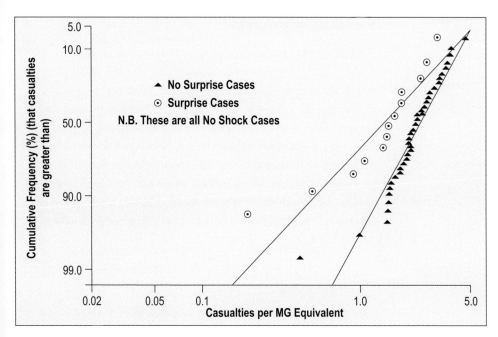

Figure 7.1
The Effect of Surprise onCasualties per Defensive MG

assumptions. This was taken into account by dealing with all actions in a uniform manner, although some of the information came from different sources. With the other effects removed, the effect of surprise on the basic value of casualties per machine gun equivalent can be most clearly seen when the data was portrayed graphically, as in Figure 7.1 above.

From this basis it was possible to compare defence effectiveness as described in Chapter 3 for battles with and without attack surprise of the defence, comparing the two subsets of data to attain a simple ratio of defence effectiveness being reduced by approximately 0.6 when surprise was achieved, a significant difference on these samples. This, however, may not be a final answer; it can be hypothesised that the effects of surprise may be larger for low force ratio attacks. When examined for this, the available results show evidence of such a trend below 3:1 force ratio, but not, given the size of the sample, sufficient evidence to be a significant difference. Thus this remains an area where more data collection and analysis are ultimately required.

Surprise in Armoured Combat

We then turned to tank versus tank actions, but at this time the study of armour-anti-armour degradation had not taken place and so the simple basis taken for this part of the surprise study was to examine the relatively 'pure' tank versus tank actions, mainly between British and German forces in North Africa in 1941-43. This was a particularly suitable theatre because of its overall balance, with the two sides alternately taking the offensive and thus providing a corresponding balance of tactical battles. A large number of actions other than those used in this work were considered, but they were rejected for the following reasons:

a. No tank versus tank action occurred, although in the light of the later degradation studies these should perhaps be reconsidered!

b. No tank casualties occurred to either side.

c. Uncertainty about the values of key aspects of the required data.

d. Initial analysis showed that other (non-armour) weapons could have dominated the action.

In spite of these exclusions, the effect of anti-tank guns was often significant, as we have already seen, and had to be allowed for in the attribution of casualties, where historical data permitted.

A total of 55 actions were analysed and the database includes the following categories of data for each of the actions considered:

a. Initial numbers and types of tank on each side and their losses in the action.

b. Whether or not Surprise was achieved and by which side.

c. Which side was 'successful'. i.e. achieved its objective.

d. Experience level of troops on each side (simply as 0/0.5/1). This was because combat trials indicated more likelihood of experience effects for armour/anti-armour than for infantry battles.

The basic numbers of tanks and losses in each action and their types do not take account of the "quality" of different types of tank and so use was made of the same tank values or Q factors used in Chapter 5 (see also Appendix B). These values were applied to the basic data to give initial numbers of tanks and casualties in terms of these Tank Values. It should, however, be noted that initial analysis showed the findings were not greatly changed if just basic numbers of tanks were considered, given the broad similarity of tank characteristics in the Western Desert campaign. Another point to note is that the term casualties in this section refers to those tanks that were damaged or destroyed in action and does not include those that were just captured, ie we were considering battle casualties and not total tank losses.

An initial analysis attempted to take account of experience using the above judgements on experience level. However, application of these did not improve the experimental relationship of the casualty data with the other factors (Surprise, No Surprise) being considered. This may have been because the judgement of experience was too coarse to reflect the range and types of experience which actually existed. There was, however, a trend to greater probability of being surprised at low experience levels. Another preliminary analysis also showed that the effect of different types of action, viz Encounter (meeting engagements) and Non-Encounter (set piece) battles, was not statistically significant in most cases (8 out of 10). For Encounter actions the Attacker was defined as the side achieving surprise and, where there was no surprise, as the numerically superior side. Hence, the basic data was pooled into just three categories of action - the Attacker achieving surprise, the Defender achieving surprise, and where there was No Surprise. In cases where the Defender took the initiative and achieved Surprise, the original "Defender" has been deemed the "Attacker" for the purposes of calculations and in the presentation of results, except in those cases where it is explicitly labelled "with respect the original Attacker". These ad hoc modifications of the attacker/ defender definitions were each tested for homogeneity with the simple cases before being regrouped. Having achieved this simplification, we could consider

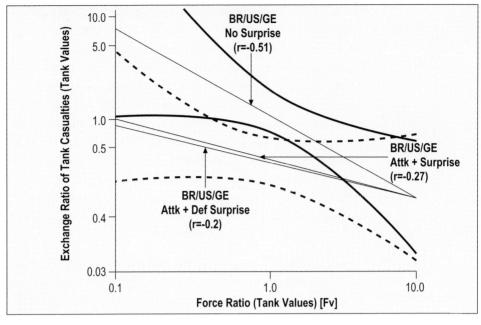

Figure 7.2
Effects of force ratio (tank values) on exchange ratio (tank values), regression lines and the associated 95% confidence limits

all 55 battles in two larger samples for analysis and reporting instead of dealing with five or six separate smaller samples.

Using the pooled data sets, the analysis of British, US, and German data is summarised in graph form above.

This shows how Attacker/Defender casualty exchange ratio decreases with initial force ratio (both these parameters are in Tank Values), for the three categories of action. It also shows that the achievement of Surprise, by either Attacker or Defender has a significant effect on casualty exchange ratio, reducing it by a factor of about 3 at a 1:1 initial force ratio. The regression lines do suggest, however, that at high force ratios the effect of Surprise is diminished and has no effect (i.e. a factor of 1) at about a 10:1 initial force ratio. This is more clearly illustrated in Figure 7.3 opposite.

In addition to its effects on casualties, those on success were also integrated in this part of the study. From the basic data it was possible to draw some broad indications of the effect of Attacker/ Defender force ratio and the achievement of Surprise on the chance of Success. The analysis is summarised in Figure 7.4. Here Success means the achievement by one side or the other of its stated goal,

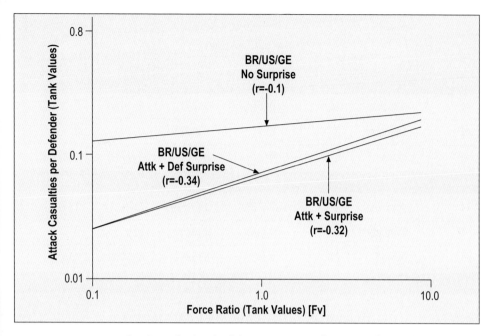

Attack Casualties per Defender (Tank Values)

Force Ratio (Tank Values) [Fv]

BR/US/GE
No Surprise
(r=-0.1)

BR/US/GE
Attk + Def Surprise
(r=-0.34)

BR/US/GE
Attk + Surprise
(r=-0.32)

Figure 7.3
Effects of force ratio
(tank values) on attack
casualties- per
defender (tank values),
regression lines

that is at the level of the action. In a few cases the result of the action was judged as a successful outcome for both sides. Although this may appear contradictory at first sight, it is possible for each side to have independent objectives and achieve them.

The results show the importance to the attacker of achieving surprise at low Attacker/Defender force ratios. At force ratios of less than unity, attacks were successful on 65% of occasions when surprise was achieved and were never solely successful without it, although in one case both sides were successful without either gaining surprise. Even though based on small samples, the result is statistically significant, at the 1% level (1 tailed t-test).*

* Random variability is characteristic of many real-world phenomena. When it occurs it is highly desirable that an objective test should be used to judge whether an observed difference between two sample means is likely to be genuine, or whether it could have arisen simply due to chance variation. The "t" statistic compares the observed difference between two means with the extent of the variation within each sample. The higher the value of this statistic, the less likely is it to have arisen purely by chance. From "t" one can compute the "significance level", or actual probability that the difference between the means could have arisen just from random variation.

Attack/ Defence Force Ratio	Achievement of Surprise	Sample Size	Success			
			Attacker	Defender	Both	None
<1	Attacker	14	9 (65%)	3 (21%)	2 (14%)	0
<1	Defender	2	0	2 (100%)	0	0
<1	None	6	0	4 (66%)	1 (17%)	1 (17%)
<1	Total	22	9 (41%)	9 (41%)	3 (14%)	1 (4%)
>1	Attacker	9	7 (78%)	1 (11%)	0	1 (11%)
>1	Defender	3	1 (33%)	2 (67%)	0	0
>1	None	21	9 (43%)	8 (38%)	3 (14%)	1 (5%)
>1	Total	33	17 (52%)	11 (33%)	3 (9%)	2 (6%)

Figure 7.4
Force ratios, surprise and success (with respect to original attacker)

At force ratios greater than unity the achievement of surprise is less important; although not statistically significant the probability of success is still higher (78%) with surprise than without it (43%). The table also shows the importance of force ratio when surprise was not achieved. In contrast to the Attacker's lack of success at force ratios below unity, his success rate at higher force ratios was better than 40%, this result being just significant at the 5% level (1 tailed t-test).

The relationship between probability of success, force ratio and surprise was investigated further by dividing the data base, which was augmented by a further set of samples, into two sets for each of the categories Attack Surprise, Attack or Defence Surprise and No Surprise. The two sets were formed by different groupings of the same set of results; the groupings each had a mean force ratio and were chosen to give reasonable samples from which to calculate probability of Success throughout the full range of force ratios (0.14 to 9.4). Where one side had suffered no casualties the exchange ratio was calculated by adding 1 to each side's casualties, ie Red losses + 1/Blue losses + 1.

The force ratio values used to plot the points in Figure 7.5 are the geometric mean points of all the values lying in each of the ranges

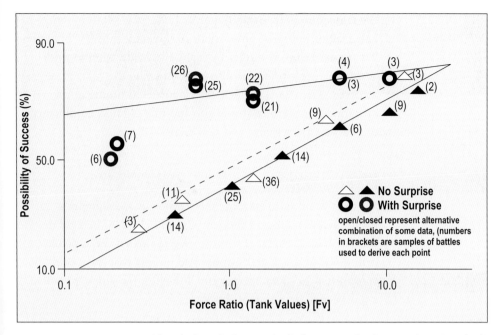

Figure 7.5
The probability of the side with surprise (attacker or defender) achieving success compared to attack success with no surprise (including additional data). (lines are best fit by eye)

considered. Attack Success includes not only those actions in which just the Attacker (the side with Surprise) was successful, but also actions which were a success for both sides, although in these cases success was attributed to just one side and not both.

The graph compares either Attack or Defence Surprise (i.e. with Surprise) against the No Surprise results. These results add confirmation to the view that with surprise the probability of success is largely independent of force ratio but without surprise it is highly dependent on it. They also enable comparisons to be made at selected values of force ratios, e.g. at 1:1 force ratio the probability of success is about 40% without surprise and 70% with it while at 3:1 the corresponding probabilities are 54% and 76%.

In individual cases the probability of achieving surprise will vary with deployments, commanders' expectations, and the initiative and competence of each side; its achievement is one output of a complicated two-sided contest. In spite of this disclaimer, it was worth examining the incidence of surprise in the variety of real but imperfect conditions that occur in combat. Hence, in a simple aside to the main study of the effects of surprise we also checked the same sample of battles to test its frequency. Both infantry and armour indicated proportions in the range 40-50% of battles. This could be taken further by examining wider samples with adequate casualty data and also by considering the types of surprise achieved. These include such characteristics as timing of the operation, direction of attack, size and mix of force, employment of new weapon systems, and new tactics.

Shock

We then went on to examine shock. Broadly speaking, this phenomenon represents those aspects of behaviour beyond the simple physical effects of surprise. We compared the available definitions of shock and surprise and, noting that there could be confusion over causal mechanism and effect for shock, proposed a provisional definition of shock as:

> 'Morale conditions causing stunning, paralysis or debilitating effect either on the performance of individuals in combat or on an organisation in combat. It is noted that this could include effects normally ascribed to more individual definitions, such as the state caused by massed mounted attack, indirect impact of the mobile arm, closing with the enemy and crushing him, surprise, and the employment of concentrated fire power.'

This was then reconsidered in the light of further military definitions of shock, a psychological review of shock, and a search for historical examples and their review by a psychologist.

The military term for shock was derived from the direct (striking) use of club, sword, spear or bayonet as shock weapons as distinct from arrows, bullets or shells, which are missile weapons. We examined the extension of this through the shock action of cavalry to that of armour through identifying historical examples.

Taking infantry first, we noted three factors that influenced the ability of attacking foot soldiers to inflict shock. First, the charging distance was limited by the individual's ability to run laden with weapons and equipment and was usually never beyond 100 metres. In cases where this was exceeded it was because the enemy had already broken and was being pursued. In these instances, it was not uncommon for the pursuit on foot to continue up to half a mile or so. Visibility, too, was significant. Several shock inducing infantry attacks took place at night, in half light, or in mist, enabling the attackers to be protected from view until the last possible moment. Likewise, in good visibility intelligent use of the ground also provided concealment. We were also struck by the use of battle cries, cheers, and yells. While there is no doubt that these helped to instil confidence among the attackers, they also appear to have been instrumental in throwing the defenders into disarray, especially when combined with the visibility factor.

While attacking infantry was often assisted by the supporting fire of artillery, mortars, and machine guns, and, in more recent cases, airpower as well, it was noticeable that the bayonet often played a major role. Paddy Griffith, commenting on the US Civil War, remarked:

> "The aim of the bayonet charge was to destroy the cohesion of an enemy unit and chase it away. Any casualties which might be inflicted on it in the process were seen as incidental to the main purpose of breaking the solidarity of its line. Hence the bayonet was not intended as a weapon for killing, like the rifle, but as a weapon for winning decisive results."[1]

An example from the Boer War graphically supports this thesis. It took place during the Battle of Colenso in December 1899:

> "The South Lancashire Regiment had halted pinned to the ground by Boer fire… In an instant there appeared to the left of the Boer trench, a dozen - only a dozen - violent forms rushing forward. A small party had worked their way to the flank, and were at close quarters with cold steel. And then - by contrast to their former courage - the valiant burgers fled in all directions, and others held out their rifles and bandoliers and begged for mercy, which was sometimes generously given, so that by the time the whole attack had charged forward into me trenches there was a nice string of thirty two prisoners winding down the hill……"[2]

The fact that few casualties are inflicted by the bayonet is also born out by the experience of World War 2. Indeed, it is the psychological effect of the threat of cold steel which so often makes a man surrender or run away.

Turning now to horsed cavalry, its ultimate role is well summed up by the Marquis of Anglesey in the opening volume of his magisterial history of British Cavalry:

> "To be able, with speed, to manoeuvre a number of horsemen into a well-dressed line; to throw that line at a wavering enemy with shattering rapidity; thus, in an instant, to smash all opposition, imposing irreversible disintegration, and, finally, to pursue with relentless vigour …"[3]

In other words, the cavalry use of shock action to achieve its objective and success was often dependent on the timing of the charge. Charging distance was also crucial. To begin the flat out assault too far away from the objective resulted in a loss of cohesion, since it became difficult to maintain formation with the horses at full gallop. On the other hand, a certain interval was required in order to develop the necessary momentum. Consequently, we found that most successful charges did not take place under 200 metres away and at no more than 500 metres from the objective. Even then, the first half of the distance was covered at the trot.

World War 1 saw the armoured fighting vehicle (AFV) begin to supersede the horsed cavalryman, whose days had become increasingly numbered through the development of rapid fire weapons. Its first significant employment as a shock weapon was at Cambrai on 20 November 1917. An eyewitness description:

> "The night was very dark, with a dense ground mist, but so complete were all the arrangements that this caused no inconvenience, while it helped to screen the massing of this unparalleled armada. A sudden burst of shelling and trench mortar fire from the German lines startled every one and provoked suspicions of a premature discovery, but it died away in half an hour. From five o'clock until zero hour the whole front was quiet. At ten minutes past six tanks and infantry

began to move; and at 6.20, with the sky lightening rapidly above the mist, the barrage exploded with a shattering crash of sound along the German outpost line, some 250 yards in front of the "advance guard" machines (tanks) … The immediate onset of the tanks inevitability was overwhelming. The German outposts, dazed or annihilated were overrun in an instant … The defenders of the front trench, scrambling out of dug-outs and shelters to meet the crash and flame of the barrage, saw the leading tanks almost upon them, their appearance made the more grotesque and terrifying by the huge black bundles (fascines) they carried on their cabs. As these tanks swung left-handed and fired down into the trench, others also surmounted by these appalling objects appeared in multitudes behind them out of the mist … The great fascines were loosed and rolled over the parapet to the trench floor; and down the whole line tanks were dipping and rearing up and clawing their way across into the almost unravaged country beyond. The defenders of the line were running panic-stricken, casting away arms and equipment … Our following infantry had found little to do beyond firing on the fugitives and rounding up gangs of half-stupefied prisoners. It was now broad daylight, the mist was thinning, and everywhere from Havrincourt to Banteux on the canal was rout and consternation."[4]

It was a situation which would be recreated many times during World War 2, especially given the dramatic increases in the mobility and firepower of the tank. The shock effect that it produced as been defined as:

"… the combination of the destructive physical and psychological effect on the enemy produced by the violent impact of mounted and mobile armor – protected firepower of tanks and supporting mechanised troops. Armor combines tremendous concentrated firepower with rapid movement of its fighting vehicles to produce severe shock effect on the enemy. The shock effect of armor increases greatly as the number of tanks employed in mass is employed. This shock effect, in a properly executed armor assault, can have a decidedly adverse effect on enemy morale and a favourable effect on friendly troops' morale."[5]

Figure 7.6
First classification of
military 'shock' by
cause

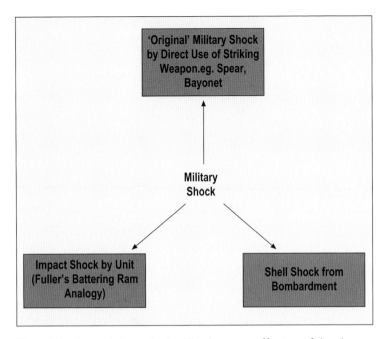

Yet, while the tank is undoubtedly the most effective of the three shock instruments reviewed, it became apparent to us that the perceptions of the tank commander as to its shock effect are much less strong than those of the horseman or infantryman with rifle and bayonet. Part of the reason for this is that tank crews have more limited vision and are also insulated to a degree by their armoured protection from what is going on around them. The greater speed of the tank means that there is less time to take in what is happening and the tank commander's attention is also concentrated to a significant degree on potential threats to him in the form of other tanks and anti-tank weapons.

Major General J F C Fuller, whose writings on the use of armour had a seminal role on the development of armoured warfare between the two world wars, looked at shock in terms of mechanics.[6] He extended the analogy through the applied mechanics of impact, using the battering ram as an example. Effectively, this also represents the extension of shock from a weapon's impact to a unit's impact and the components of momentum from applied mechanics, mass and velocity figure explicitly into his examples. It is relevant to note that Fuller stresses the importance of shock being used against something solid, yet not too solid, to be effective. This itself offers a good direct analogy to the destruction of hard crystalline structures, such as rocks, by impact. If the energy or momentum is above a certain level relative to the mass of the rock it will be shattered, whereas below this only local fragmentation damage will occur. This analogy then, together with the distinct, but militarily and psychologically accepted shell shock, forms two distinct classes of shock from the third, original military use of personal "shock weapons". This is best summarised in a diagram opposite (Figure 7.6).

The next step was to arrange for a psychological review of the different concepts of shock. This stressed the ambiguity of the everyday use of the word, where it can be used to convey different things. Shock is used to convey the sense of outrage; indignation or disgust which may be felt or expressed when confronted by something which seems improper or scandalous. It is often used synonymously with moral indignation. Another sense is that of a sudden and disturbing physical or mental impression, often brought about by upsetting and unanticipated news such as an accident or bereavement. Another use of the word has been to describe a state of sudden and severe prostration, which may have bee attributed to over simulation of the nervous system as a consequence of sudden pain or violent emotions. This use of the word may often be used to describe the psychological and physical consequences of injury - "he died of shock" or "the shock was more dangerous than the loss of blood".

A review of the literature concerning the psychological concept of shock revealed a lack of an operational definition. To a large extent it derives meaning from two of the aspects mentioned in everyday use - the response to a sudden overwhelming event and the state of prostration following over-stimulation of the nervous system as a consequence of intense emotion or pain. Its condition can be defined as cognitive, emotional and physiological dysfunction as a consequence of exposure to overwhelming stress. This is a transient state, however, which will subside if the stressors are removed but which may progress to physical or psychological illness if the stress is sustained.

As such, the concept represents a spectrum of intensity of response dependent upon differences between individuals, stimulus characteristics and situational variables and is best approached from the perspective of literature on stress and, in particular, the effects of fear.

Individuals who are shocked are in a state of impaired function often to the extent of being unable to care effectively for their own safety or to take notice of events going on around them. There is no single description which can illustrate the condition of shock but, rather, there are a series of possible characteristics of being shocked. Some of the effects may be characterised as:

 a. *Emotional* There is often marked emotional impairment with flattening of mood or emotional liability being present, some people reporting intense anxiety. Individuals may vary from being totally unresponsive to crying wildly.

 b. *Cognitive* There may be reduced awareness of events going on around the individual. Powers of concentration and the ability to reason logically are impaired and there may be repeated intrusive thoughts of a frightening or distressing nature. Some people, however, report feelings of depersonalisation and unreality.

 c. *Behavioural* The individual may show signs of restlessness with extreme startled responses, there may be uncontrollable tremor and impairment of skilled motor responses. Some individuals may engage in stereotyped motor responses or may respond with hostility and violence while others become immobile and apathetic.

The symptoms described above can occur at various degrees of severity. Being in a state of shock is not an all or nothing state, rather it can be seen as a continuum of impairment of cognition, emotional and behavioural responses, with some showing mild impairment while others are totally incapacitated.

The military concept of shock can embrace both individual behaviour and that of an organisation, in particular, the command and communications network. The recognition by military planners of the significance of shock is summed up in General Sir John Hackett's assertion that the results of all land battles have been determined by the number of people who run away. To be able to induce soldiers to run or be otherwise unable to fight has been an aim of much military strategy. Indeed, the term "shock tactics" owes its origins to the recognition of the impact of a cavalry charge on infantry positions. The German infiltration tactics employed during their 1918 offensives on the Western Front and their World War 2 Blitzkrieg operations demonstrated the advantages of the use of shock troops for rapid advance with a corresponding paralysis of an enemy's ability to respond efficiently.

It is perhaps in the Soviet approach that the military concept of shock is exemplified. Their military made extensive study of the likely effects of stress on both individuals and organisations. There was widespread recognition that the effects of stresses such as fear, fatigue, pain and surprise can render an individual unable to function in the absence of any physical injury. When the build up of these stresses is particularly rapid both the individual and the organisation are liable to be in a state of shock The term used for this corresponds with the medical term for an apoplectic stroke or heart attack and conveys a sense of paralysis.

One of the foremost Western experts on Soviet military thought, Christopher Donnelly, contended that it is this "battlefield paralysis of will" that was the aim of Soviet commanders. Rather than a slow war of attrition, the aim was to deliver a shock to the enemy by virtue of surprise and the intensity of attack. This would be accompanied by a rapid advance deep into the rear, leaving the enemy paralysed and unable to react. Once undermined and destabilised, the defence would be deprived of its collective strength even though individual units were still viable.[7]

The Soviets saw the element of surprise as being particularly important in causing shock. In such situations, once an attack had occurred, the enemy would be rendered incapable of processing the amount of information it would likely receive in a very short period of time. At the same time, attacks would occur throughout the depth of enemy positions with particular emphasis on destruction of the command and communications network, further paralysing the defence. The ability to communicate would be additionally hampered by electronic attack. Accompanying this would be the use of rumour and psychological warfare. This approach would increase the stress on both the individual and organisation. The continuation of pressure would also prevent both the organisation and the individual from being able to rest, recover and reorganise. There was also a recognition that particular weapons and tactics could increase the shock value of an attack. The use of the unexpected such as smoke screens and flamethrowers were expected to have a high shock value, as would the use of or even the threat of chemical weapons.

Perhaps most of all, the Soviets placed high value on the effects of heavy bombardment in producing a state of shock, with weapons such as the multi-barrelled rocket launcher being exploited for the shock value as much as killing power. They expected defenders would be in a state of paralysis and unable to respond for some time following intensive heavy bombardment. Indeed, Soviet doctrine did not assume that more than 25 per cent of those under such a bombardment would be killed or wounded.

Experiences during World War 2 suggest that shock can certainly occur as a result of artillery fire. German tank crews subjected to intense bombardment for over two hours during the Normandy battles were reported to be in a state of severe shock and incapable of offering resistance. Indeed, during the bombardment individuals were known to have attempted suicide rather than face continued shelling. Anecdotal accounts suggest that intensity and duration of shelling are directly related to the development of a state of shock. The amount of noise and smoke which weapons emit are also thought to be related to the degree of fear which they inspire. The experience of a near miss has also been suggested as a powerful determinant of being shocked. Related to this the unpredictability of fire, when it is not possible to tell when the next round is coming or where it will land. Indeed, prolonged indirect fire does have a significant effect. Interviews with British and American servicemen who were World War 2 veterans established that some 95% feared artillery and mortar fire the most.[8] Similar results were obtained for the Korean War.[9] Indeed, the main effects of bombardment are the generation of extreme fear and a feeling of helplessness. Individuals are forced to take cover and, as a consequence, are unable to observe the enemy or return fire. With noise reaching a near paralysing level it is not possible to communicate or engage in any activity other than waiting and enduring.

A complementary approach to the psychological review was to search for examples from battles where an additional effect, over and above what might be expected from previous assessments of combat degradation, was present. An exhaustive search of the literature was not possible, given the available resources, and so data from previous work was used, as well as that from other current work. In all, 174 infantry attacks, 77 cavalry charges, and 102 armoured attacks were examined, with the assistance of historians.

Extreme changes in battle behaviour were identified in a number of cases. One involved a charge by elements an Austrian lancer regiment during the 1866 Battle of Custozza, in which the Austrians decisively defeated the Italians. Exactly 103 men took part in the charge against an advancing Italian infantry brigade, 5,000 men strong, and scattered it. Having broken through one regiment, the lancers made for the commander and his staff, wounding the former and his deputy and depriving the brigade of its leadership at the critical juncture. It was the decisive moment in the battle. Three instances concerned Axis troops during Rommel's assault on the Alamein Line in early July 1942. On the opening day of the assault the German 90th Light Division, one of Rommel's crack formations, broke in the face of a concentrated barrage. Two days later, the best of the Italian divisions suffered a similar fate, as Barrie Pitt describes:

> "Ariete, the one Italian formation -in whom he (Rommel) felt some confidence, had set off ... unescorted by Trieste ... Just short of Alam Nayil, Ariete came under heavy shell fire from the same batteries which the previous day had cooperated so efficiently in halting the panzer division, and while the Italian gunners were endeavouring both to answer the foe and dig

themselves in, they were suddenly struck in the flank first by mortar, anti-tank and machine gun 'fire, and then by a storming bayonet charge by a complete battalion of New Zealanders (19th Battalion, 4th Brigade) which overran them, captured forty-four of their guns, took three hundred and fifty prisoners and large numbers of soft skinned vehicles … and as the rest of Ariete Division drew back, it was caught again in flank by 4th Armoured Brigade. By now Generale de Division Balotta was despondently reporting to Rommel that his command had been reduced to five Ml3 medium tanks and two guns. The odd part of this catastrophe was that an armoured division and the best formation his Italian allies could supply - had been virtually destroyed by one infantry battalion and attached artillery … .' [10]

Finally, on 4 July, 15th Panzer Division was caught in the process of a withdrawal by tanks of the British 22nd Armoured Brigade. Panic resulted among the overstrained Germans. These three instances must be put in the context of a force that had been fighting unceasingly for five weeks as it drove the British Eighth Army back from Gazala to el Alamein and was undoubtedly reaching the point of exhaustion.

In a different context was the so-called Manston Mutiny in August 1940 during the Battle of Britain. Manston was one of RAF Fighter Command's forward airfields in Kent and was subjected to persistent attack by the Luftwaffe. At the height of the bombing, some 100 new ground staff had arrived, but there was no opportunity to get them settled. Consequently, they and others sought shelter in the labyrinth of caves under the airfield and refused to come out. Officers, too, succumbed to the strain of the ceaseless raids on Manston:

"By now, after four all-out raids, few buildings were even tenable. With all water cut off, men shaved at the pre-war swimming pool - if they shaved at all. Many were close to breaking point; in the nick of time Squadron Leader James Leathart, 54 Squadron, stopped an overwrought technical officer firing blind down the shelters to flush the scrimshankers out. Manston's chaplain, the Reverend Cecil King, acted as promptly. Near-beserk, another

THE STRESS OF BATTLE

officer had burst wild-eyed into the mess, a revolver trembling in his had, threatening to finish off himself and every man present. Gently, King led him from the room, talking of God's infinite mercy, until the man broke down and surrendered his gun."[11]

A separate search for examples of shock caused by tanks provided two battles, which were analysed in detail.[12] The first was an attack by British infantry against Italian colonial troops at Gallabat in Sudan in November 1940 after it had been seized by the Italians four months earlier. Eleven out of the twelve supporting tanks were knocked out, but the attack was a success. The key appears to have been when the tanks crashed through the walls of the fort, causing many of the defenders to flee. When the Italians counter-attacked, the presence of the surviving tank ensured that the single company holding the fort repulsed it. The second concerned an attack by the 3rd King's Own Hussars on German positions in front of Citta di Castello in Italy on 21 July 1944. The attack was made without infantry support across terrain that the Germans believed to be unsuitable for tanks. The defending unit, 741 Jaeger Regiment, suffered heavy casualties and was forced to fall back behind Citta di Castello. The crew of the one German anti-tank gun present panicked and abandoned their gun to hide in a farm house when they first saw the Hussars' tanks, although they did return a few hours later and knocked out three tanks before being killed.

Shock and Panic

When these selected examples of relevant cases of an extra effect found in battle in the search for shock were put to the psychologist who had produced the review outlined above, a new distinction arose. He judged the majority of these examples to be 'panic' rather than 'shock'. Panic is a state of loss of control brought about by extreme fear or terror. It is characterised by intense fear, disorganisation, physiological arousal and attempts at flight and avoidance. It is particularly interesting to note that panic had not been differentiated in any military, historical or psychological writing relevant to shock or mentioned in the psychological review of shock, but it was immediately raised on psychological review of actual examples of combat behaviour. Before making specific comments upon the examples and showing why they are, in the main, considered illustrative of 'panic' it is worth discussing the psychological aspects of panic and how it might occur.

Panic occurs in individuals either on an occasional or frequent basis. It is a state which also affects groups of people. Panic in groups is not merely individual panic multiplied but rather a group phenomenon with differing causal factors. It is therefore worth looking at individual and group panic separately.

Intense fear reduces the ability to process information with a consequent narrowing in perceived alternatives in terms of responses. The course of action which individuals may take is in part determined by their perceived alternatives, which in turn may be decided by what others around them are doing. A feature of many panic states is the attempt at flight or avoidance behaviour. We all experience panic as a noxious state while flight or avoidance brings immediate but only temporary reduction in the state of discomfort. Flight in states of intense fear is something which, in terms of the individual, may have been both positively reinforced by others around him running away or negatively reinforced by these neighbours standing their ground. It may become an enduring behaviour.

Panic is essentially an immediate response to a sudden and intense fear inducing situation. The effects of fear in terms of arousal and hyperventilation make a state of panic more likely in susceptible individuals. This susceptibility may well be inherited. Certainly animal studies have demonstrated that panic behaviour may be selectively bred into strains of rats and dogs. Panic involves flight or at least the attempt to flee. Animals in a state of panic which attempt escape but are unable to flee often become shocked and even die suddenly. The panic of the rabbit caught in the car's headlights quickly turns to shock when its paralysis prevents it from trying to evade the threat. Indeed, the relationship between panic and shock is probably a temporal one. Panic is an instant response to intense fear brought about by unexpected events characterised by disorganisation, arousal and flight. Shock occurs in more prolonged exposure to fear inducing stimuli when responding is not possible or is unlikely to be effective. Shock also occurs when the fear inducing stimulus is of sufficiently high intensity. It may well be that individual differences either in physiology or perception determine individual states of panic versus shock. If the stressor is of sufficient intensity or of a prolonged duration then shock is likely as a consequence.

The military concept of shock and the use of shock troops or shock cavalry is likely to encompass both states of panic and shock. Certainly the shock which these military tactics hoped to induce was often a disorganised rout which often may have been a state of group panic. In the example of panic occurring in groups, size of group, ratio of leaders to led and styles of leadership are important. Although there are instances when panic has appeared contagious, where group solidarity is strong, panic as a group phenomena is unlikely to occur. The weaker group cohesion is the greater likelihood of panic.

The separation of cause and effect, the separation of organisational from individual effect and distinguishing between panic and shock are shown diagrammatically in Figures 7.7 and 7.8.

Thus the long used but vaguely defined term of shock has been traced to a series of actions and effects in three broad classes - shock/striking weapons, shell shock, and impact shock. All of these have been found to be sometimes associated with psychological effects, either separately or in conjunction. In addition, impact shock has been shown to cause a panic effect on occasion, a distinctly different effect from shock.

Shell Shock from Bombardment

Considering practical cases, the shell shock effect of bombardment has been examined from historical data as "post-bombardment suppression". The effect has been measured. It can be significant and is related to density and duration of bombardment

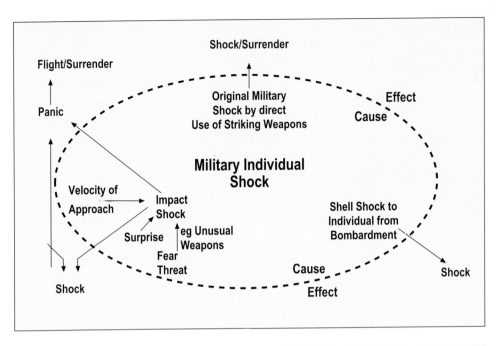

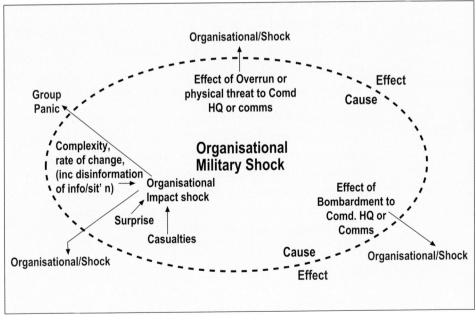

(see Figure 3.6). Moreover, the relationship is corroborated by close agreement in the working range with independent Soviet battle norms, which were the result of extensive analysis of World

Figure 7.7
Division of military
shock (and panic)
by cause and effect
Individual Military
Shock

Figure 7.8
Division of Military
Shock (and panic)
by cause and effect
Organisational Military
Shock

War 2 Eastern Front data. Hence, this effect, now appropriately named, is adequately described for modelling. The only extra work needed was to estimate the post-bombardment recovery time with the interval following the end of the bombardment; given the application of the existing relationship to fire at attackers following "close behind" a bombardment. This noted that delays in the attacker following up behind the barrage brought about an equivalent defender recovery time, but this was not considered critical to the main study.

An analogous effect would be the bombardment of defenders by the direct fire of tanks during the assault. Again, this has been examined as "suppression" and quantified from historical data in the chapter on small arms degradation. This allows adequate gaming and modelling relationships to be derived and is generically similar to the artillery bombardment effect, where the relationship between suppressive effect and weight of fire (in this case as attack tanks facing each defence weapon) takes a negative exponential form. In other words, defence effectiveness is continuously reduced as the bombardment increases, but the rate of reduction also reduces so that effectiveness never actually reaches zero.

Impact Shock

The other group of functional cases of identifiable effect relate mainly to impact shock but may include components due to original (striking) shock or to shell shock. Effects of impact shock are related to the effect of a charge against or rapid approach towards the defence by a force with threatening weapons in the form of infantry with bayonets, cavalry, tanks, and strafing aircraft. Any of these may cause a mixture of shock and panic effects. Before going on to discuss these, it is useful to compare the causes and effects of panic and shock, which are summarised in Figure 7.9.

In a first analysis of the occurrence of these effects we decided that the available combat data was insufficient to treat shock and panic separately and so looked at the broad class of effects separately of infantry, cavalry and armour attack. First, the conditions for

	Shock	Panic
Cause	Exposure to sudden and overwhelming stress, overstimulation of the nervous system.	Extreme fear or terror Hyperventilation
Duration	Development depends on intensity of terror, can be persistent.	Instant Response, Limited Duration
Nature	Progressive effect	On/Off effect
Effect on behaviour	Reduced awareness	Reduced ability to process info
	Passivity or restlessness with extreme startle response	Physical arousal Flight avoidance

Figure 7.9
Comparison of shock and panic

(Given the inter-relationship between the occurrence of panic and shock shown in Figs 7.7 and 7.8 this simplification cannot represent all the aspects nor the change from one to the other; when the cause of panic increases or cannot be avoided panic can be replaced by shock.)

achieving shock were explored using the historian's judgement of when it occurred and then, having identified the major causes, an attempt was made to quantify their effects on combat effectiveness. Three separate sets of battles, mainly at battalion or regimental level, were examined:

a. attacks by tanks or by forces which included tanks.

b. attacks by cavalry (to explore the "rapid approach" threat).

c. attacks by infantry.

Before embarking upon any quantitative analysis it is worth illustrating the very large shock effects that armoured attacks can have by quoting from two sources, which describe the so called Rumanian "tank panic" during the decisive Soviet counter-offensive at Stalingrad in the second half of November 1942, which cut off the German Sixth Army in the city:

"Fourth Panzer Army recorded that the Rumanian Corps disintegrated so rapidly that all measures to stop the fleeing troops became useless before they could be put into execution. At nightfall the army concluded that by morning the Rumanian

VI Corps would have no combat value worth mentioning. Hoth reported that what had taken weeks to achieve had been ruined in a day; in many places the Rumanians had offered no resistance –they had fallen victim to an indescribable tank panic." [13]

And:

"But the Rumanians soon found themselves faced with a situation they were not up to. They fell victim to what Guderian has called 'tank fright', the panic which seizes units inexperienced in operations against armour. Enemy tanks, which had broken through the line, suddenly appeared from behind attacking. A cry went up: 'Enemy tanks in the rear!' Panic followed." [14]

Analysis of Shock When Facing Armoured Attack

Using our sample of 102 tank attack actions, we analysed it in detail in order to determine which of the following factors caused shock to occur:

a. Achievement of surprise.

b. The presence of 'invulnerable' tanks in the attack - due mainly to the lack of effective anti-tank weapons in the defence or their belief in their weapons' ineffectiveness.

c. Poor visibility, including terrain limitations.

d. Speed of attack.

The results are best illustrated by Venn diagrams. These showed that the existence of surprise was the dominant factor. Hence, the sample was sub divided to assess the impact of the other three factors in the absence of and the presence of surprise.

Of 60 cases without surprise (see Figure 7.10), 26 did not reflect poor visibility, invulnerable tanks, or shock and only 14 (23%) showed shock, with the majority due to the presence of 'invulnerable' tanks. Poor visibility, in the absence of surprise, gave no increase in the probability of shock. For all cases without 'invulnerable' tanks in the attack and without surprise the probability of shock was assessed as approximately 10 per cent (i.e. 4 cases in

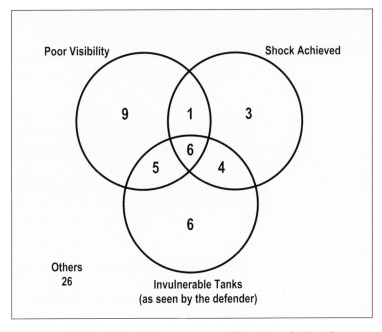

Figure 7.10
Armoured Attacks with
No surprise (60 cases)

Poor Visibility

Shock Achieved

9   1   3

6

5   4

6

Others
26

Invulnerable Tanks
(as seen by the defender)

39 actions). The effect of the presence of 'invulnerable' tanks, without surprise, was to increase this probability to approximately 50 per cent (10 cases out of 21) when all visibility and morale states were pooled. The difference between the estimates of 10 per cent and 50 per cent (without and with invulnerable tanks) is statistically significant at better than the 1% level. This increase broadly represents the effect of 'tank panic' as illustrated in the Rumanian example described above.

When surprise is achieved, the occurrence of shock becomes much more frequent (see Figure 7.11). Of 42 cases with surprise, 35 (83%) (pooling all visibilities, morale factors, and both vulnerable and invulnerable tanks) showed shock. This result is significantly different from the 23 per cent no surprise probability at the 0.1% level. When the factors of visibility, vulnerability and surprise are examined in various combinations sample sizes are small, but a consistent pattern emerges with probabilities of shock occurring varying from 60 to 90 per cent. The lowest probability of 60 per cent is based on the effect of surprise alone, that is, an attack against a strong defence made without invulnerable tanks and in good visibility.

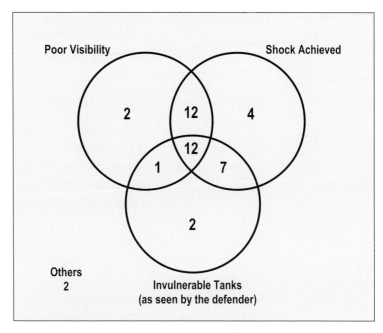

Figure 7.11
Armoured cases with surprise (42 cases)

Poor Visibility   Shock Achieved

2   12   4

12

1   7

2

Others
2

Invulnerable Tanks
(as seen by the defender)

The consistent pattern of probabilities of shock which emerges is summarised below:

Figure 7.12
Shock effects on defence with surprise

Conditions of Tank Attack	Probability of Shock
Surprise Alone	0.27
Surprise + Invulnerable Tanks	0.70
Surprise + Poor Visibility	0.85
Surprise + Invulnerable Tanks + Poor Visibility	0.90
Surprise + All The Above	0.95

In order to examine further combined effects, the data was tested on a simple model which assumed that each potential extra cause had an independent conditional probability of causing shock, given surprise. If this hypothesis is correct then the probability of shock occurring with surprise and another condition can be estimated by multiplying together the conditional probabilities of no shock for each and deducting the product from one. The process yields the estimates shown in Figure 7.12. The individual probabilities agree well with the direct empirical data although sample sizes are too small to test the sub groups (i.e. the hypothesis explains the results but is not statistically confirmed).

Analysis of Shock when Facing Cavalry Attack

We then turned to horsed cavalry. On the face of it, there might appear to be little value in studying cavalry actions, as this type of attack has long been superseded by armoured assaults. However, by studying less complex cavalry attacks, it is easier to see more clearly the workings of the fundamental processes which still underlie armoured attacks in the more complex modern battlefield. While invulnerability is not particularly relevant to the cavalry, but a key factor for armour, armoured attacks are often noted for their lack of speed. Thus, a study of the cavalry allows an assessment of the effect of attack speed, which is masked by other effects in armoured attacks. In effect, therefore, the study of cavalry underpins the work carried out on armoured attacks.

For possible shock factors, we considered the following when examining the sample of 77 cavalry actions:

a. Achievement of surprise.

b. Poor visibility, including terrain limitations.

c. Speed of attack.

By considering the basic data with the aid of Venn diagrams it was again found that the achievement of surprise was an important factor in causing shock. In the 50 actions in which surprise was achieved, 44 (88%) resulted in shock compared with only nine (33%) in the 27 actions when surprise did not occur. This difference was statistically significant at the 0.1% level. Examination of the surprise and no surprise actions separately, again using Venn diagrams, showed that neither defence morale nor visibility had a significant effect on the probability of the occurrence of shock. The largest difference was between the surprise/poor visibility and surprise/good visibility samples which yielded probabilities of 94% and 78% respectively which was similar to the pattern in tank attacks; but even this difference was not statistically significant on the sample sizes considered here.

Speed of attack was included as a factor to be examined following a review of many published works on cavalry history. These suggested, inter alia, that faster charges from 200 metres were more likely to shock than slower ones. The French cavalry seemed to have galloped at 10 mph in the final charge, whereas most other nationalities galloped at 15 mph. Thus both the surprise and no-surprise samples were split into two further sub-sets: fast attacks, that is, at the gallop, by non-French nationalities, and slow attacks, that is French attacks, or attacks recorded as being slower by non-French forces.

The results of the examination of attack speed as a factor showed that when surprise was not achieved, shock occurred in nine out of the 17 fast attacks, but it was judged never to have been caused in the 10 slow attacks. This difference is statistically significant at the 5% level. However, for cases with surprise, an increase in attack speed did not have the effect of increasing the probability of shock, as the latter was already high at 88%. In summary, the two important alternative factors causing shock in cavalry attacks are surprise and speed of attack.

Analysis Of Shock When Facing Infantry Attacks

Turning to infantry attacks, the military historian Paddy Griffith is in no doubt of the shock effect of a bayonet charge:

> "A great deal of misunderstanding has arisen from the fact that a 'bayonet charge' could be highly effective even without a bayonet actually touching an enemy soldier, let alone killing him. One hundred percent of the casualties might be caused by musketry, yet the bayonet could still be the instrument of victory. This was because its purpose was not to kill soldiers but to disorganise regiments and win ground. It was the flourish of the bayonet and the determination in the eyes of its owner that on some occasions produced "Shock", just as on others the same effect might be produced by noise or muzzle flash".[15]

A total of 174 actions, from the 18th Century to the 1982 Falklands War, were used and the factors examined were again the achievement of surprise and poor visibility. The bayonet appears to have played a noteworthy part in several of the examples, the action by the South Lancashires at Colenso cited earlier being just one of these. While surprise was the dominant factor in causing shock, it was surprise in combination with other factors, which by themselves did not increase the probability of shock, which was important. The two other factors isolated were defence morale and poor visibility. With any one of these factors, including surprise, or none of them the probability of shock was 15 per cent. However, the combination of surprise with either low defence morale or poor visibility increased this to approximately 50 per cent. Thus, surprise appeared to act as a catalyst for the extra effect of either of the others.

Analysis of Shock when Facing Dive Air Attacks

In terms of air attack, the shock (suppressive) effects of air bombardment had already been included in the assessment of artillery and the results summarised in Chapter 4. However, an additional air case in the form of the dive attack has been studied as a result of anecdotal evidence and also because it characterises the "rapid approach threat". Effects on both infantry and armour have been claimed as consequences of dive attack. These have been investigated, concentrating mainly on the influence of World War 2 attacks by rocket firing Hawker Typhoons, for which there is good data, on subsequent ground combat and some post-combat surveys.

The reduction in defence infantry effectiveness after a Typhoon dive attack was investigated by comparing a set of appropriate battles with the results of previous historical analysis assessments in which dive air attack had not featured. This comparison showed a reduction in defence effectiveness after an air attack significant at the 1% level; the mean reduction was by a factor of approximately 56%. The comparison also indicated that this figure was relatively insensitive to the interval between air and ground attacks, the duration of the air attack (between 10 minutes and 48 hours), and to the number of sorties flown. As these results relate to a small sample, they should be treated with caution. Nevertheless, they do indicate a major effect from dive air attack, confirming many subjective comments. The effect, however, is similar to that due to shock caused by ground attacks.

A further effect was discernible from attacks on AFVs in which material damage was found to be much lower than claimed by pilots, as we have seen from the example of Mortain in August 1944, which was cited in Chapter 1. However, in addition to the confirmed material damage it was found that dive air attacks had a significant demoralising effect on AFV crews, which caused vehicle abandonment to be as significant as true vehicle casualties.

A non-combat example provides a useful introduction. In his autobiographical 'Ruins in the Sky' Fawcett recounts his experience flying with an experienced pilot in a light aircraft in South America after they had found a landing ground staked to prevent landing or endanger an aircraft attempting to land. The account illustrates the effects of unarmed aircraft:

> "He then proceeded to 'buzz' them, and years of experience as a combat flier in the Spanish Civil War and in South America went into that 'buzzing'. Terrified donkeys unseated their riders into luxuriant growths of (xigni-xigni) cactus; women and children crawled under the protection of rocks; dogs scuttled with their tails between their legs into the bush; men and youths took to their heels, leaping, running and stumbling from the vicinity of the paths. The chaos could not have been greater had the Beechcraft sprouted a hail of machine gun bullets." [16]

The first and principal effect of air attack on ground troops in World War 2 was that by German dive-bombers, mainly the Ju87 Stuka, but also the earlier biplane, the Henschel 123. In Poland in 1939, German pilots discovered that varying the Henschel's engine setting while flying just over ground level resulted in a shattering noise that induced panic in horse-equipped Polish formations. Demoralised, some Polish troops abandoned their positions and weapons and fled the battlefield.[17] The Ju87 was equipped with a siren and the Frenchman Marc Bloch recorded:

'Nobody who has ever heard the whistling scream made by dive bombers before releasing their load is ever likely to forget the experience … No matter how thickly the bombs may be sown, they never, in fact, register hits on more than a relatively small number of men. But the effect of bombing on the nerves is far-reaching, and can break the potential of resistance over a large area.'[18]

Later in World War 2, the main theme of morale effects from air attack emerged from the effect of British Typhoon attacks on the Germans. These used rockets, bombs, and cannon fire, but again the significant factor was the dive attack. The debriefing of German prisoners of war revealed that strafing attacks by aircraft using either machine guns or rockets caused the greatest effect on ground troops.[19] This was for two reasons:

a. The aircraft in a strafing run is aimed at the target and individuals seemed to feel it was aimed personally at them. The dive attack of aircraft such as Stukas, Typhoons or their modem counterparts produces a rapidly approaching threat analogous to the cavalry charge.

b. The great speed and small size of certain projectiles, particularly machine gun bullets and rockets, compared to large cumbersome projectiles such as bombs, meant that it was almost impossible to anticipate the trajectory and point of impact.

Yet, trials with rocket firing Typhoons revealed that they had an accuracy of a mere five per cent and in combat their attacks were recorded as being most horrific to the targets at weapon release as the rockets ignited. The effect on AFV crews was often to cause them to abandon their vehicles, as was seen at Mortain, when virtually the same number of tanks were abandoned or destroyed by their crews as were knocked out by rockets. Indeed, the hypothetical Impact Shock model of conditions indicates similar values being achieved for the Stuka and Typhoon at weapon release to the value for cavalry beginning the gallop for an effective charge.

Generalising the Effect of Approach Velocity on Impact Shock

Integral to Impact Shock is how the individual reacts to the perceived threat. Some investigation had been done into the behaviour of humans and animals. For instance, in the United States psychologists performed tests on infants aged 6-20 days. Foam rubber cubes of two sizes approached to points close to the subjects at constant velocity and at varying angles of approach Their responses were observed at various distances, but became so violent at closer ranges that the experiment had to be halted.[20]

The effect on real combat performance is, of course, less easily tested, but some general indications are possible. Our studies of cavalry charges showed that, with surprise absent, the speed of the charge was a significant factor in causing shock to the defence. The size of the approaching threat is also relevant. From this visual impact, there will be a critical distance. Up to the critical distance the motion of the attacker will not cause the defender great distress, but, should the attacker continue towards the defender at less than the critical distance, the defender will perceive that impact is inevitable and he must either flee immediately or stand and fight. Given that the approach of a threatening object is discerned as a common factor, it may be hypothesised that the critical measurement for an instantaneous reaction is rate of change of solid angle subtended by the threat, with respect to time. The Impact Value for visual impact has therefore been expressed by the following formula:

$$\text{Solid angle Subtended} = \frac{\text{Presented Area}}{(\text{Critical Distance})^2} = \frac{A}{X^2}$$

Where A = Presented area, X = Critical Distance

To obtain the rate of change of Solid Angle with time, that is the Impact Value, this expression needs to be differentiated with respect to time:

$$\text{Hypothetical Impact Value} = -2 \times \frac{(A)}{(X^3)} \frac{dX}{dt}$$

$$\text{Hypothetical Impact Value} = \text{Constant} \times \frac{\text{Presented Area}}{(\text{Critical Distance})^3} \times \text{Approach Velocity}$$

Figure 7.13
Estimates of
hypothetical impact
shock factor

By considering the historical data on approaching military threats, we are now able to calculate the impact shock values of various types of attack.

ATTACKER & CONDITION	EFFECTIVE RANGE	APPROACH VELOCITY V(m/SEC)	FRONTAL AREA A(m²)	HYPOTHETICAL IMPACT SHOCK AV/D3(SEC⁻¹)
ATTACKS IN CONDITIONS SHOWN TO GIVE SHOCK EFFECT				
BRITISH CAVALRY AT START OF GALLOP	180	6.7	2.0	2.2 X 10⁻⁶ (*1)
GERMAN Ju 87 STUKA AT BOMB RELEASE	880m Slant Range and 800m Altitude	180	7.1	1.85 x 10⁻⁶
BRITISH TYPHOON AT ROCKET FIRING	900m Slant Range and 300m Altitude	220	5.75	1.75 x 10⁻⁶
ATTACKS BY OTHER WEAPONS AT DISTANCE TO PRODUCE IMPACT SHOCK FACTOR OF 2 x 10⁻⁶				
INFANTRY CHARGE { 100m (*2) 120m (*2)		1.8 3	1.0 1.0	
WWI MK V TANK	190m	1.5	9	
SHERMAN TANK	320m	9	7.3	2 x 10⁻⁶
CENTURION TANK	340m	9	9	
CHALLENGER TANK	450m	18	10	

*1. The French attack with a slower gallop would have a similar factor, but would have travelled 40m closer.

*2. Or when they start to charge, if it is at a shorter range. Griffith's historical research on ranges used for fire and subsequent charge in the US Civil War notes mean quoted engagement ranges of 70-140m and quotes their distances of defence breaking to infantry attack as between 10 and 100m.[21]

Wider Considerations in Factors Affecting Shock

This impact shock 'model' only examines the physical dimensions of the approaching threat, however, and review of historical

THE STRESS OF BATTLE

examples suggested that other elements of the approaching threat contribute to the effect produced on the defender. These include noise, which can be especially threatening in conditions of poor visibility. There is, too, the generation of noise as a psychological weapon to shock the enemy. Historically, drums, trumpets and cymbals were used to achieve this explicit aim; more recently the addition of wooden propellers to the Stuka dive bomber and whistles attached to its bombs were developed with this in mind. This aspect of shock is often cited as achieved by weapons, even where it has not been explicitly developed or enhanced; the noise associated with the motion/firing of various systems such as galloping cavalry, helicopters and tanks are good examples of this. The use of battle cries in infantry charges is another example.

Another aspect is the lethality of threat. One suggestion is that the weighting of the approaching threat should allow for not just its physical dimensions, but also should incorporate an element of its known or suspected lethality. This, however, would have to be adjusted to accommodate acclimatisation over time. For example, the Ju87 Stuka was much feared during the early part of World War 2, but troops got used to it. The German Pz VI Tiger tank also became less awesome to Allied troops when they began to recognise its vulnerabilities.

There is also the question of actual and perceived threat dimensions. Consider an approaching dust cloud. In conditions of general battlefield dust, the critical dimensions are those of the dust cloud which the defender perceives as generated by the threat itself. Future work might seek to establish further resolution within this effect, ie to determine to what degree the sight of, say, a line of tanks at the bottom/leading edge of a dust cloud is regarded as more threatening than the same size dust cloud which completely envelopes the tanks or from the leading edge of which only gun barrels are seen to emerge. There are also historical instances where the generation of dust clouds has been used to confuse the enemy's perception of the disposition and numbers of vehicles it is facing, ie Rommel's use of aero engines for generating dust at the Battle of Gazala in May 1942. Such techniques were also enshrined in Soviet doctrine within the broad heading of "Maskirovka" (literally deception). Confusion and the associated shock caused by dust clouds, whether actual or generated, could cause shock at an operational level as well as tactical impact shock.

The same is possibly true with mist, although the relationship between impact shock effect and mist in situations in which troops are facing tanks is difficult to assess due to the conflicting nature of historical observations. In the case of the battle of Amiens in August 1918, the evidence is insufficient to confirm the Australian official historian's comment that the impact shock effect of the tanks was at its most effective not when the mist was allowing visibility of up to ten yards, but when the range was between 100 and 200 yards. An account of the forcing of the Argenta Gap in April 1945, during the final stage of the Italian campaign, suggests that the Churchill tanks advancing in the mist caused German surrenders (although partly occasioned by surprise) and that the opposition noticeably stiffened as the mist thinned and lifted.[22]

It is worth considering the psychological impact of mist and smoke on a defender. For example, does he perceive it as a "wall" protecting him from the sight of the enemy or does he perceive it as the leading edge of an unknown and unseen enemy? The way in which this "barrier" is perceived must be taken into account when its effect is represented in the model. It may be that there is an Optimum Visibility Distance, which is the boundary between the senses of safety and fear and this will depend on what a defender feels he can achieve and what he thinks the attacker can achieve, once he emerges into the open. This is obviously a variant on the "critical distance" defined in the basic (good visibility) model.

The three apparently different causes of shock, rapid approach, surprise, and an 'invulnerable attack' do have a common component; they each induce in the defence a feeling of helplessness, in the first two the inability to respond in time, the last to respond at all. Although the main factors causing shock and panic effects have been isolated, other factors possibly causing or accelerating shock have been noted in some cases:

THE STRESS OF BATTLE

a. An approaching threat indicated by sound as well, or instead of sight (and exploited by fitting sirens to Stuka dive bombers).

b. The contagious effects of panic, so that the threshold of panic within a group may be set by that of a few members of the group.

c. The surprise of attacking forces (e.g. by counter attack, sudden direct or indirect fire) leading to panic.

d. The effects of inexperience, fatigue and depleted forces which may leave units more susceptible to panic and shock.

Quantifying the Immediate Effect of Shock

As for combat degradation, a first estimate of the immediate effect of shock by ground attack is a further mean reduction in defence effectiveness by a factor 65%, this difference being significant at the 1% level (1 tail t-test). Combining this result with the similar sample of battles evaluated after dive air attack, and showing a mean reduction of effectiveness by a factor of 56%, gives a pooled mean reduction by a factor of 60%.

Wider Effects

Following the immediate reduction in combat effectiveness there is a period of disruption, the duration and development of which will depend on subsequent enemy action and on the ability of the command and control organisation to rally and reinvigorate the troops. At the tactical level, the primary effect is best characterised as a temporary loss of cohesion and individual effectiveness. The consequence of this depends on the other side's exploitation, that is whether it takes full advantage of the effect or not. If it does not, there may be little noticeable long-term effect resulting from either bombardment or impact shock. Because the long term effects depend very much on subsequent events it was considered best to combine further study of these effects of shock at the campaign level, rather than attempt to follow through the variety of the poorly described and chaotic events at low level.

Furthermore, The similarity in the low-level effects of morale and visibility on the achievement of shock could enhance the understanding of the effects of these factors at the operational level.

The Incidence and Effects of Shock at the Operational Level

As it happened, a parallel study was examining breakthroughs at the operational level. An initial qualitative analysis of the 99 battles being studied tested groups of successful breakthrough operations to determine which factors were most frequently associated with success. In a list of 30 postulated factors, shock was ranked third, behind two categories of surprise, for achieving breakthrough, and sixth for achieving subsequent campaign success. The rankings of the ten most important factors associated with achieving breakthrough and campaign success are shown below, the positions being based on comparisons of the frequency of association of each factor with successful and unsuccessful campaigns.

Figure 7.14
Factors associated with breakthrough success

Ranking Order	Breakthrough	Subsequent Success
1	Initial Surprise	Attack Air Superiority
2	Subsequent Surprise	Subsequent Surprise
3	Shock	Mobility
4	Attack Air Superiority	Defence C3
5	Attack Recce	Attack Recce
6	Attack Artillery Superiority	Shock
7	Attack Defence C3	Defence Reserves
8	Attack Intelligence	Attack Artillery Superiority
9	Mobility	Initial Surprise
10	Defence Type	Attack Logistics Capability

It is relevant to remember that the presence of shock was assessed for each campaign by the historian who researched the campaigns, along with the other qualitative factors. A test on the correlation of this judged factor, with cases found to have an extra unexplained sensitivity, could therefore lead to extra understanding of the causes of shock (here taken in its general definition and not distinguished from panic).

Thirty-three of the 99 campaigns selected for analysis were judged by the historian to include defence shock, with breakthroughs occurring in all of them. As might be expected, the judged occurrence of shock appeared to be highly correlated with surprise. Of 62 operations with surprise, 30 (49%) showed shock, compared to only three (8%) of the 37 without surprise. Chi-squared testing shows that this difference is statistically significant at better than the 1% level.

The combined effect of surprise and weak defence morale was then reviewed for its association with shock. Thirty-seven of the campaigns featured this characteristic and the interrelationship between weaker morale and showing surprise and shock is shown in the Venn diagram in Figure 7.15. It can be seen that out of the 33 shock cases 17 (52%) featured both surprise and weaker defence morale. Although another 13 cases of shock were associated with surprise alone, no shock cases were associated with weak morale alone, indicating that surprise is the key but that weak defence morale may exacerbate the situation. This can be tested by comparing the proportion of campaigns with surprise showing shock in groups with and without identified weak defence morale. Of 35 campaigns with surprise, but without weak morale, 13 (37%) showed shock but of 27 with surprise and weak morale 17 (63%) showed shock, a significant difference at the 5% level. This confirms that although surprise is directly linked to shock it is also rendered far more effective against a weaker defence morale.

The association of weak morale with shock still left a residue of 13 cases of high morale in defence, with both surprise and shock present but with no other *prima facie* cause of shock identified. We thought it possible that shell shock might have resulted from the combined effects of artillery superiority and surprise and found that artillery superiority alone has little association with shock, but

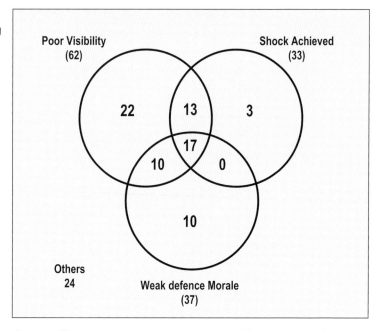

Figure 7.15
Venn Diagram showing association of surprise and weak defence morale with shock

Poor Visibility (62)

Shock Achieved (33)

22   13   3

17

10   0

10

Others
24

Weak defence Morale (37)

that its effect on campaigns with surprise offered the possibility of a weak link. Thus the conditional probability of shock given surprise was 48% overall, 43% without artillery superiority and 51% with. This is not a significant trend at the 5% level, but the artillery association was to be tested with quantitative measures when they became available. A similar test on the effect of air superiority also showed no more significance to defence shock - it changed the 49% conditional probability of shock given surprise to 52% with air superiority against 43% without.

In the context of the infliction of panic, we looked at the attackers' sudden appearance at close range to the defence, due either to terrain or to poor visibility. This pointed to the possibility of testing for the effect of visibility on shock. An extra prompt to this was provided by the association noted between poor visibility at breakthrough with conditional probability of subsequent success given a breakthrough. No obvious explanation existed for this unless perhaps the initial poor visibility led to some longer term effect, such as shock to the defending force, persisting after breakthrough.

Figure 7.16
Venn Diagram showing
association of surprise
and poor visibility with
shock

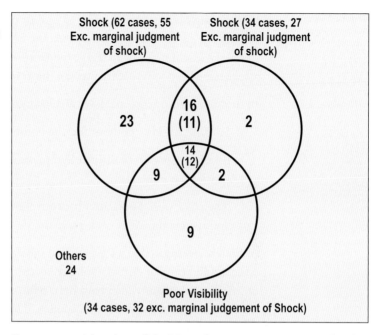

Shock (62 cases, 55
Exc. marginal judgment
of shock)

Shock (34 cases, 27
Exc. marginal judgment
of shock)

23

16
(11)

2

9

14
(12)

2

9

Others
24

Poor Visibility
(34 cases, 32 exc. marginal judgement of Shock)

Even so, consideration of the Venn diagram in Figure 7.16 for the combined association of surprise, poor visibility and shock shows that 16 (14 plus 2) of the 34 cases of poor visibility were also judged to show shock and the majority of them, 14, were linked with surprise. Thus the conditional probability of shock given surprise was 41% (16/39) in good visibility and 61% (14/23) in poor visibility, This difference was only significant at the 10% level, but if seven cases of marginal judgements of shock are removed, then it is significant at the 5% level.

Considering these two associations of shock with surprise and poor morale and shock with surprise and poor visibility it is worth noting that each association tends to be related to a different breakthrough type. Thus, of 17 cases of immediate break- through (ie those taking less than half a day) which were linked to shock, all 17 had achieved surprise, 13 (76%) were associated with defence morale and 7 (41%) with poor visibility, In contrast, of 16 cases of quick or prolonged breakthrough (ie those taking more than half a day), 13 (81%) had surprise but only 4 (25%) were associated with poor defence morale and 9 (56%) occurred in poor visibility (See Figure 7.16). Given surprise and shock, the trend that immediate breakthrough is more easily achieved against poor defence morale was statistically significant at better than the 5% level. The observed trend of breakthroughs which take longer to achieve being associated with poor visibility was not, however significant.

In summary, the operational level investigation confirmed that:

a. Surprise is a key condition for the occurrence of shock.

b. The combination of surprise and poor defence morale makes shock even more likely.

c. There is a weak association between the occurrence of shock and the combination of surprise and poor visibility.

Although investigated in a separate and subsequent study to the estimation of combat degradation, the effects of shock and surprise on combat behaviour which have been estimated represent extra reductions on performance in real combat. The estimation of these effects is relevant to this history because their isolation helps to reduce the unexplained parts of variability in combat performance. It also provides examples of different approaches to analysis of historical data. Perhaps most importantly, however, is that the large effects of surprise and shock have now been separated and estimated quantitatively, thus replacing the previous subjective and unsatisfactory estimates of their effectiveness.

SOURCE REFERENCES

[1] Griffith, Paddy *Battle in the Civil War* p40 Fieldbooks, London, 1986

[2] Churchill, W S *The Boer War: London to Ladysmith* p199 Leo Cooper/ Octopus, London edition, 1990

[3] Anglesey, Marquis of *A History of British Cavalry 1816-1850* p95 Leo Cooper, London, 1973

[4] Captain D G Browne quoted in Liddell Hart, B H *The Tanks: Volume One 1914-1939* pp136-7 Cassell, London, 1959

[5] *The History and Role of Armor* US Armor Branch, Fort Knox Ky, 1968

[6] Bacon Adm Sir R, Fuller Maj Gen J F C, Playfair Air Marshal Sir P ed *Warfare Today* Odhams, London, c1944

[7] Donnelly, Christopher *The Soviet Attitude to Stress in Battle* Journal of the Royal Army Medical Corps No 128 pp72-78

[8] Naylor, JC A *Proposed method for Determining the Psychological Effects of Weapons* 1st Symposium on Psychological Effects of Non-Nuclear Weapons, Elgin AFB, 1964

[9] Donovan, G N *The Use of Infantry Weapons and Equipment in Korea* John Hopkins University, 1952

[10] Pitt, Barrie *Crucible of War* p144 Cape, London, 1982

[11] Collier, Richard *Eagle Day* p144 Hodder & Stoughton, London, 1966

[12] Goodman, RC Tank Shock CORDA Reports Ref. CD 1089/TR 1.0, 2.0, 1989

[13] Ziemke, E.F *Stalingrad to Berlin: The German Defeat in the East* p53 US Army Center for Military History, 1968

[14] Carell, Paul *Hitler Moves East 1941-43* p625 Bantam Books, London, 1966

[15] Griffith, Paddy *Rally Once Again* p141 Crowood Press, Ramsbury, 1989

[16] Fawcett, B *Ruins in the Sky* Hutchinson, London, 1958

[17] Hallion, R P *Strike From the Sky* p133 Smithsonian Institute Press, 1989

[18] Ibid p141

[19] 1944 POW interrogation Reports on the Effects of Air Attack (ADI (K) Report No 382/1944) in AIR 37/36, National Archives, Kew

[20] Bower, T G R, Broughton, T M, Moore, M K in *Perception & Psychophysics* Vol 9, 1970

[21] Griffith, Paddy *Battle in the Civil War* op cit

[22] Perrett, Bryan 1980 *The Churchill Tank* Osprey, London, 1980

CHAPTER EIGHT
Conclusion

Military OA and the Use of Field Trials

This volume has been written to trace the development of UK historical analysis within military operational analysis. It has been set against the background of the overall evolution of military operational analysis in World War 2 and in the changed needs for such advice in the post-1945 defence environment.

Military OA evolved to meet urgent operational needs to optimise weapons effectiveness in battle and had to function within the confines of the short timescales inherent in war. It operated by using empirical data, including early lessons and simple analysis from ongoing and recent combat, and by applying simple theory. In the post-war situation the pressure to aid ongoing military operations was reduced, but the techniques of analysis were still needed to inform the development of new equipment and new operational concepts. To this end, the emphasis was changed to include more wargaming and more complicated modelling studies to advise on the future uses of alternative developments. Direct OA advice on current operations did continue, but only at a local level within the relevant commands.

When it came to the development of new weapons systems, data on their application in war was derived increasingly from individuals' military experience and peacetime trials of various types. The DOAE Field Studies Division conducted a wide variety of such studies, including trials, exercise monitoring, map studies, and tactical exercises without troops (TEWTs). In the 1970s, the development of pulsed laser weapon simulators and the increased utility of portable instrumentation on both AFVs and men enabled extra realisation to be applied to field manoeuvres. They allowed real-time force-on-force exercises to be conducted and monitored in detail and the resultant database, made up of quasi-battles involving realistic forces and terrain, as well as realtime interactions, provided the scope for extensive analysis.

The analysis of interactions and events within several hundred of such battles, enabled advice to be given on more realistic OA combat modelling. Among the aspects covered were the differences between range firing and quasi-combat situation exercises, and the events and interactions between deployed forces which limited their effectiveness in these situations. Casualty estimates and the variability between the use of individual weapons could also be derived. This last aspect was more important than might be expected, since most real battles take place in unique sets of conditions. Trials-derived estimates permitted attribution of the division of combat outcomes between definable conditions and the chance variations, something which would simply not have been possible from combat data alone. Yet, while this type of analysis did enable us to get closer to the real world of combat, we recognised only too well that there were obvious significant differences between this and simulated combat, however sophisticated. The question was the degree of difference between the competitive play with real-time interaction and that with the additional imposition of live fire conditions.

The Approach to Historical Analysis of Close Combat

Sample results from individual battles have long been quoted anecdotally, but there has been a major problem in their more rigorous use. This, as has already been mentioned, is the stochastic or chance variation associated with a single real-world event, combined with the variety of conditions of battle, so that each is effectively unique. Without a knowledge of the framework of the effects due to varying conditions, it would have been much more difficult to find a basis on which to attempt to group the unique results from each. This may be considered to have been demonstrated in part by the paucity of quantitative analysis in this area.

A solution was, however, possible. From trials we now had estimates, of the scales of some effects, of conditions such as force ratio and open or close country. We also had an estimate for the target level of residual variability, as the introduction of more variables, in successive subsets of battles, refined our comparison. We could apply these same factors (such as force ratio, experience and close country) to real battles and compare the results. Nonetheless, it was still necessary to start with samples of simple battles, with few weapon types and little suppressive fire, and to introduce their effects progressively in later samples. Hence, we began with machine guns and rifles, whose characteristics and performance have not changed markedly over the years.

Using this approach, it was possible to develop comparisons between the levels of effectiveness in simulated and real combat and to establish basic combat degradation estimates, one weapon class at a time. From this the extra effects of suppression, surprise and shock, among other influences, could also be deduced from progressively increased samples of battles. We began with relatively simple battles, where suppression, surprise and shock, for example, were not evident and compared these with separate subsets which included one of these conditions. We then moved on to find another robust set reflecting another of the conditions. This enabled us to isolate the effects of each and evaluate them, although the exercise did prove more complicated for shock because of its intimate connection with surprise.

The net result of this approach has been the ability to make empirical estimates of effects which other techniques and disciplines had been unable to tackle or quantify. This initial study thus represented a prototype of a new technique, which we termed 'historical analysis', for developing general relationships for behaviour and effectiveness in combat. While HA is related to the World War 2 analysis of individual operations, to assist with plans for subsequent similar operations, it differs from the latter in that HA is a research activity offering generally applicable results, whereas the World War 2 OA was applied development to provide limited answers in very short timescales and usually to very specific questions.

Historical Analysis and History

Here it is worth attempting to consider historical analysis as it emerged and to distinguish it from military history *per se* and from operational analysis, to which HA offers data and relationships.

Clearly, there is a close association between history and HA, but a major division among historians has become apparent. Some believe that each event is a unique result of a unique combination of circumstances from which only a skilled historian may offer a distillation of qualitative comments; others accept that these combinations form part of a pattern and may be susceptible to statistical or quantitative analysis. Part of the problem is that some historians tend to adopt a subjective approach and the situation becomes that described by Tolstoi in Chapter 1, namely a variety of interpretations, often contradictory, of the same event. Even those historians prepared to accept the possibility of extracting general quantitative lessons from history hesitate to adopt such an approach. This is either because they consider that a sufficiency of material is available to maintain their conventional study techniques or that through their training and discipline they are simply not versed in quantitative analysis.

Historical Analysis is distinct from pure history in that it uses data from history to conduct empirical modelling and statistical analysis. It is a scientific process employing historical data as an input and is interdisciplinary in the academic sense. As with OA, HA requires a scientific approach, but a background knowledge of military history, especially at the operational level, and the ability to interpret historical data for analysis are also essential. Hence, HA does require close working with historians, who not only provide the historical data but also advise on the selection of samples for study and on the limits of available data. An important difference from many historical roles, however, is the necessity to separate objective data for analysis from historians' opinions, although the latter, together with military opinion, can help to offer hypotheses for HA study.*

As a consequence of this use of history, the acceptance of HA by historians has been divided into those that welcome this extra objective use of history and those that tend to suspect its trespass on

---

* It is worth noting here that an historian's assessment of a condition, such as surprise and shock, is an intermediate case and can offer useful assessment for initial analysis as a prelude to further, more objective data collection.

the supremacy of historians' expert judgement. However, over the years we have been able to assemble a group of military historians who are both supportive of HA and capable of working with the necessary self-discipline. Indeed, they agree with the Tolstoi dictum that "instead of seeking for causes, History takes as its problem the search for laws … Along this route all the human sciences have travelled".

Widening HA to Anti-Tank Combat

Returning to the combat degradation investigations, once we had established major degradation factors for dismounted infantry in combat, we needed to answer a further question before the infantry factor could be included in models. An equivalent factor (or factors) for armour/anti-armour combat needed to be established, since a model representing degradation of one weapon class but not the other could cause great distortion in studies, whether of force mix or of posture.

The process developed for the analysis of infantry combat was not immediately applicable to the analysis of armour/anti-armour combat. The battles were smaller in terms of weapon numbers, and more variable. There were also greater variations in weapons (e.g. tanks and anti-tank guns, each with a wide range of capabilities). Furthermore, the main combat data from World War 2 was not paralleled by combat trials with equivalent equipment, since the trials had only used equipment contemporary in 1975, which could not be readily compared with weapons of thirty years earlier.

An extra step necessary to break into this area was the detailed historical study of a sample of anti-tank battles. The resulting detailed reconstructions led to further insight into the mechanism of combat degradation, in particular the disproportionate contribution of a heroic minority, which proved possible to quantify. This left two other groups of weapon crews each of significantly different performance, with one group performing at a low level relative to the heroes and the remainder failing to participate in engagements, even when presented with targets. Thus, the overall degradation of infantry could now be represented, with an equivalent factor for anti-tank weapons, but there was an additional aspect introduced in their division into three groups by effectiveness, rather than as one continuous distribution.

Tank and Anti-Tank

This research also led into more detailed understanding of the other factors governing effectiveness: the variation of the probability of heroism with rank and the first assessment of surprise on weapon crew participation. The result of the detailed anti-tank assessments also allowed direct comparisons of these weapons and tanks in the anti-tank role. The results were surprising and conflicted with many expert opinions, both military and those of historians, in showing guns in this role to be two to three times more effective than tanks despite their physical disadvantages and relative simplicity and cheapness. The difference could be explained by crew make-up in terms of both rank and numbers. This finding applied to tank killing only and not to the tank's other capabilities, especially in the offensive, capabilities which could not be achieved by anti-gun guns. It did however indicate an area where many published histories have implicitly caused distortion by omitting data on numbers of anti-tank guns whilst quoting relative numbers of tanks. This is particularly the case with the tank versus tank and anti-tank battles of the Western Desert between 1940 and 1943, where new histories including data on anti-tank weapons could offer more insight. Indeed, we had to develop histories of many of these actions for our study, although these remain unpublished.

The above has outlined the direction of study followed by the combat degradation investigation, for which it has now provided quantitative assessment and has begun to tease out some of the mechanisms of low combat effectiveness. It has also opened up other areas previously considered 'soft', that is not amenable to the provision of hard estimates or to measurement by direct observations. For example, at the tactical level the quantification of the suppressive effects of attack tanks was now possible, as were the effects of surprise and shock at both the tactical and operational level.

The Benefits of Widening HA

In widening to these other areas, another type of benefit apart from the demonstrated and established utility of HA was revealed. This was the knowledge imparted from one study to another of the factors found to be significant in combat. Not only does this help guide the selection of samples, but also gives advance knowledge of variability of data and forms of relationship to be expected. In the same way as the initial HA study was aided by comparison from combat trials, later studies benefited by experience of the earlier ones. Thus, further trials data and relationships are now less important, although they can still at times be helpful. Indeed, as HA has widened the scope of studies, especially at the higherlevels of war, the possibility of comparable trials has often been reduced. HA now covers studies ranging from the individual weapon level up to the strategic level and embraces the work of all three services in both war and other operations. It has demonstrated its ability to make quantitative assessment of the behaviour of men and organisations in real operations, where the threat of death or mutilation is ever present.

Insights into Combat Behaviour

One of the more intriguing aspects of personnel combat behaviour, which has emerged above, has been the apparent division of individuals in combat into three groups: heroic, degraded and zero effectiveness. Whilst there were also variations within each group, these were similar in scale to those observable in the one undivided group, under the no threat situation of exercise. Learning more on this and on the interactions associated with supervision, or leading by example, indicate scope for further HA study and psychological advice.

HA has also revealed factors concerning the conduct of military operations which have not previously been considered. Typical are the importance of the make up of weapon crews by rank due to the quantifiable effects of supervision and individual heroism and, at a higher level, the significance of the aggressive employment of reconnaissance elements. In both of these examples combat effectiveness can be improved significantly without a change in weapons or equipment.

The Utility of Historical Analysis

Inevitably, the answers to some questions raise others, the answers to some requiring ever greater levels of detailed research and analysis. While HA has the bonus of historical data representing an almost inexhaustible resource, the costs of extracting sufficient data to reach firm and immutable conclusions can sometimes become prohibitive. This is especially so, since in the real world the need for studies can be in the form of answers within limited time and costs. Hence, each study is a fine balance in terms of resources, although the samples and collateral from prior studies can also often provide extra value.

In reviewing the evolution of Historical Analysis at the end of Chapter 1 its role in providing outputs to operational research was discussed. As HA has developed successive relationships and factors, these have been applied both directly, as military advice to headquarters and less directly to provide assistance in OA modelling and wargaming. In these latter roles the output of HA has been usable, both in model construction and in validation of models; thus HA is playing a role in increasing the fidelity of OA models.

Theme

The overall theme of HA has been to fill the gaps in the knowledge of performance in combat; these frequently relate to human performance and reactions. The description and quantification of these, although as yet far from complete, do attest to General George S Patton's assertion that "wars may be fought with weapons, but they are won by men. It is the spirit of the men who follow and the men who lead that gains the victory."[1] In the past, operational analysis so often ignored the human element and the fact that any weapons system is only as good as the crew that mans it. Historical Analysis serves to make good this omission and so deepens our understanding of what actually happens on the battlefield.

SOURCE NOTE

[1]   *Cavalry Journal* (US) September 1933

APPENDIX A
A typical King's Ride Battle

*The Exercise KINGS RIDE series of monitored exercises included
scenarios in open country, woods and urban areas. This example from
the urban Exercise KINGS RIDE V indicates some of the detail
possible in reconstructing these interactive exercises.*

*The exercise used part of the British urban training area
'RUHLEBEN FIGHTING CITY' in Berlin in 1985 and troops
drawn from the Berlin Brigade:*
    1 Royal Hampshire Regt   B Sqn 14/20 Hussars
    38 (Berlin) Fd Sqn RE

The scenario was painted as an Orange (Warsaw Pact) motor rifle
company, supported by a tank platoon, acting as a regimental
spearhead. Its mission was to secure a key crossroads within a
village to enable a regimental attack to take place. Speed was of
the essence, and the company had been ordered to achieve its
objective within one hour. The Blue forces were represented by an
infantry platoon, organised in six fire teams, which were defending
the village. They had two tanks and two APCs in support.

The Orange commander planned a three phase attack. In the first,
No 4 Platoon, on the right, was to advance on foot along the line of
the railway embankment, cross the ditch, and secure Buildings 27
and 28. No 6 Platoon would similarly advance between Buildings
6 and 7 and, using the ditch as cover, capture Buildings 24 and 25.
Both platoons would then establish machine guns on the roofs of
these buildings to provide fire support for Phases 2 and 3. Phase 2
itself would see the tank platoon deploy with two tanks blocking
off the road junction by the railway bridge to enable them to cover
the final objective with fire, while the third took up position at
the T junction by the church and provided fire support towards
Building No 72. Simultaneously, the third platoon, No 2, was to
move by APC and dismount on the road by the church. As part
of Phase 3, this platoon would attack round behind Buildings 72
and 71, securing the houses on that side of the street. This would

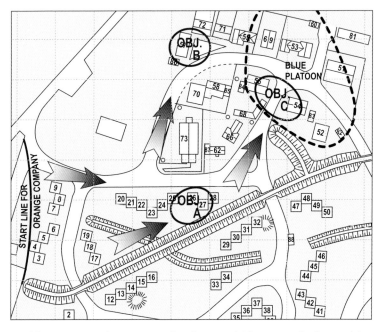

Figure A1
Outline map of sample scenario (Ex. KINGS RIDE V)

enable it to provide covering fire for No 6 Platoon, which would attack from the area of the church to seize Building No 56. At the same time, No 4 Platoon would attack over the embankment spur and secure Building 54.

The Blue defence was close around the final objective. Platoon HQ was in Building No 56, although the platoon sergeant was in Building No 52. The platoon's two LAWs were outside Buildings 51 and 69 covering the roads running from the south and west into the crossroads. These two roads had also been cratered, with each containing anti-tank mines. Barbed wire also covered the platoon position. The supporting tanks and APCs were positioned on the north-east outskirts of the village.

Orange began with Nos 4 and 6 Platoons dismounted and No 2 Platoon still in its BMPs and preparing to move behind the tank platoon. The company commander had positioned himself with No 6 Platoon. Within three minutes, Nos 4 and 6 Platoons had reached their Phase 1 objectives and were establishing machine gun positions as ordered. There was some desultory Blue fire from Building 56, but this caused no casualties. The tanks now began to deploy, but as the first reached the junction by Building 66, it spotted a Blue tank by Building 51. The latter fired first and knocked the Orange tank out with its second round. The second Orange tank had now arrived and despatched the Blue tank, which had been unable to traverse its gun and engage in time.

Six minutes into the battle and Phase 3 was about to begin. Nos 4 and 6 Platoons began their final assault. Blue fire from Building 52 accounted for three men from No 4 Platoon as they crossed the railway embankment spur, while No 6 Platoon lost one man as a result of fire from Building 56. The surviving Orange tank at the road junction also began to move cautiously forwards. Two minutes later, No 4 Platoon got into Building 52 with no further casualties and accounted for three men from one of the Blue fire teams as they attempted to withdraw to Building 51. No 6 Platoon also enjoyed success, getting into Building 70 and then moving behind Building 66.

With twelve minutes now passed, No 2 Platoon was carrying out its move behind Buildings 71 and 72, but came under fire from a machine gun in the rear of Building 69 and suffered nine casualties. A Blue APC also began to move to a better position from which it could engage the attackers. Meanwhile, No 4 Platoon had consolidated its hold on Building 52 and was engaging Building 51, killing the Blue platoon sergeant in the process. Simultaneously, No 6 Platoon attacked Building 56, preventing the Blue platoon HQ and accompanying fire section from escaping. The BMPs were moving up in support, but one was destroyed by an off-route mine. Another reached the crater by Building 58 and pumped several rounds of 73mm into Building 56, which, of course, No 6 Platoon was clearing. Very fortuitously, the platoon escaped casualties and the fire killed the Blue platoon commander and two of his men. Indeed, only the fire team commander managed to escape. Elsewhere, Blue was desperately trying to adjust its defence, deploying one section from Building 51 to join the other in Building 69. Its surviving tank did, however, knock out the Orange tank which had been inching forward from the road junction. Casualties now totalled 23 Orange to ten Blue.

With No 2 Platoon still pinned down by the machine gun by Building 69, No 4 Platoon was preparing to assault Building 56. An unfortunate incident now occurred. No 4 Platoon commander had seen the remaining Blue tank and ordered one of his RPG-7 men to knock it out. There was no immediate shot from the weapon and so the commander and two of his men moved to behind the Blue tank to get a better view down the street. They closed up to the rear of the tank and then the RPG-7 finally fired, killing all three men, the rest of the platoon remaining blissfully unaware of what had happened.

While No 6 Platoon now prepared to attack Building 69, the Blue defenders were converging on Buildings 53 and 69 for a last ditch stand. The remaining Orange tank moved from the church to engage the former and one of the BMPs spotted the LAW by Building 69 and engaged it. As it did so, the LAW man moved his position to behind the house. Waiting until the BMP had fired a number of rounds, he crept forward, firing two rounds at the BMP and knocking it out with the second. By this stage, Orange casualties were 32 and Blue 15.

With 24 minutes gone, the struggling No 2 Platoon, which had lost four more men, was still trying to get into Building 55, sending one section across the barbed wire next to Building 69. No 4 Platoon, now leaderless, had made no further progress and the company commander had moved across to reorganise it. No 6 Platoon, on the other hand, continued to make good progress. From Building 56 it sent a half section into Building 53, which was quickly cleared, and another into Building 69. As it entered a room, an RPG-7 round was fired at it, killing three of the attackers. To support the attack, a BMP moved from the church to behind the surviving Orange tank. Simultaneously, a Blue APC moved up behind the destroyed Blue tank on the right, but was knocked out by a No 4 Platoon RPG-7.

No 2 Platoon eventually managed to get into Building 69, not realising that No 6 Platoon had already entered. The resultant fire fight resulted in further friendly fire casualties. With the company commander in charge, No 4 Platoon was now moving forward once more and entered Building 51. After 30 minutes, it was decided that Orange had reached its objective and the battle was halted.

In terms of casualties, Orange had suffered 60 per cent and Blue just over 85 per cent. The fact, too, that nine or ten of the 51 Orange attackers were the result of fratricide reveals how difficult command and control are, although some were undoubtedly caused by the fact that the attackers did not stick entirely to the plan. As for Orange's eventual success, the commanders on both sides agreed that the key was the speed with which the attack was carried out. It also did not help that Blue lost its platoon commander and platoon sergeant early on and it was noted that subsequently there was too much defence movement and not enough fire.

Thanks to Simfire devices and a variety of monitoring equipment, it was possible to obtain a detailed picture of exactly what had taken place and see how the individual actions influenced the overall result of the battle. Analysis over the whole range of King's Ride battles not only enabled more realistic data to be fed into combat models, but also provided further insights into combat degradation.

APPENDIX B
Q and T Factors

Since enemy losses were not attributed to individual weapon systems in World War 2, the calculation of individual weapon system effectiveness by type was not a straightforward matter. The Allied weapon systems differed in their killing power, mobility and protection, and enemy systems had varied vulnerabilities. These differences of weapon attributes had to be allowed for by computing a quality index 'Q' for each weapon system (explained in greater detail below). The intention of this 'quality index' is to allow different tanks to be compared or combined so that, for example, a tank with a quality value double that of another type of tank, would be rated as having a combat effectiveness equating to two of the lower value tanks.

Statistics, such as the force ratio and the measure of effectiveness (the number of attack casualties per defender), were computed in terms of the number of weapon systems weighted by their 'Q' indices. In order to extend this procedure to include tanks and anti-tank guns of disparate morphology, and with differing crews, a further empirically determined factor 'T' has been introduced for guns. Essentially this is used to modify the gun quality index to the scale of tank quality index, allowing for the effect of the extra qualitative factors which differ between the two classes of weapon.

The starting point for the method is a study of pure tank versus tank battles at battalion level in the Western Desert. Results of this study are given in Figure B.1 which shows attack casualties per defender versus attack to defender force ratio. Tank quality or effectiveness is allowed for by a 'quality product' which takes into account lethality, protection and mobility. For example, consider battles in which there were just two types of defending tanks, A and B, and two types of attacking tank C and D. Then the points on the tank v tank lines shown in Figure B.1 would be derived as follows:

Attack = Number of C Tank Casualties x Q_C +
Casualties/ Number of D Tank Casualties x Q_D
Defender ————————————————————————
Number of A Tanks x Q_A +
Number of B Tanks x Q_B

Force Ratio = Number of C Tanks x Q_C +
Number of D Tanks x Q_D
————————————————————————
Number of A Tanks x Q_A +
Number of B Tanks x Q_B

Where Q_A, Q_B, Q_C and Q_D are the tank quality products

For battles involving both tanks and anti-tank guns the above equations are extended to take the form:

Attack = Total Attack Tank Casualties x Q_T
Casualties/ ————————————————————————
Defender Defending Tanks x Q_T +
Defending Anti-Tank Guns x Q_{AT} x 'T'$_D$

Force Ratio = Attack Tanks x Q_T +
Attack Anti-Tank Guns x Q_{AT} x 'T'$_A$
————————————————————————
Defending Tanks x Q_T +
Defending Anti-Tank Guns x Q_{AT} x 'T'$_D$

Where Q_T is tank quality product; Q_{AT} is anti-tank gun quality product; 'T'$_D$ and 'T'$_A$ are defence and attack 'T' factors respectively. These 'T' factors are necessary to account for differences in performance between tanks and anti-tank guns which occur in real combat and are not covered by the quality products. As illustrated in Figure B.1, for battles which had tanks only in attack but tanks and anti-tank guns in defence, 'T'$_D$ is estimated by the value required to bring each battle result back to the original tank versus tank only curve.

Two baseline tank versus tank curves are shown in Figure B.1; they are for battles in which the attack achieved surprise as well as battles in which it did not. Throughout this report the 'no surprise' curve was used to provide a conservative estimate of tank/anti-tank gun equivalence. Also shown is the upper 95 % confidence limit of the no surprise curve, which can also be used to produce a simple estimate of the lower 95% confidence limit on the estimated values of T.

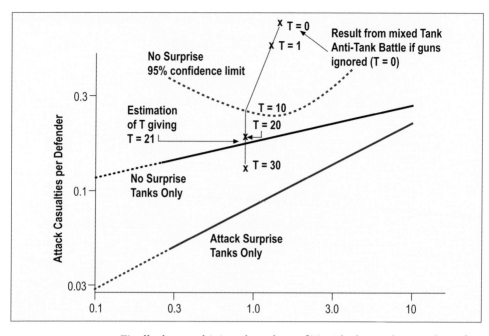

Figure B.1
Illustration of derivation of value of t factor & effects of surprise, using relationships from armoured (tank v tank) battles in the western desert

Finally, by combining the values of T with the quality products for anti-tank guns and tanks equipped with the same gun, an estimate of tank/anti-tank gun equivalence is obtained. For example, in World War 2 compare the 2 pdr anti-tank gun with a quality product of 0.96 against the Matilda II tank, equipped with the same gun, but a quality product 5.8 (reflecting greater protection and mobility). Suppose that battles which had contained both tanks and anti-tank guns in defence had yielded a mean value of 'T'$_D$ = 20. Then the number of Matilda II tanks equivalent in defence firepower to the 2 pdr anti-tank gun would be 0.96 x 20 / 5.8 = 3.3.

As already mentioned above it became apparent from the data collected during this study that in terms of overall effectiveness, a mixed defence of tanks and towed anti-tank guns, or one of guns alone, performed better for a given total of weapons, than did one composed of tanks alone, despite the lower Q indices of the towed guns. It is therefore suggested that the difference arose from the manner in which the guns were either deployed or employed. In computing the effectiveness of different weapon systems in defence the large sample of tank-only battles are used as a standard.

In these the measure of effectiveness of the defending tanks is:

Casualties per defender = (Attack tank casualties x QT)/
(Defence tanks x QT)

For mixed tank and anti-tank gun, or anti-tank gun only, defence we therefore compute:

Casualties per defender = (Attack tank casualties x Qr)/
(Defence tanks x QT +
Defence a-tk guns x QAT x T)

If 'T' in the above equation is set at 1, then it will be found that the casualty per defender statistic for mixed or gun defences is typically a good deal higher than those obtained with tanks alone. Essentially, 'T' is the extra multiplier (presumably associated with effectiveness of use) required making this last statistic equal in value to the first. 'T' has been used as the principal estimate of the effectiveness that anti-tank guns actually achieved in battle. Its use as a standard of comparison between tanks and guns does, of course, depend on the assumption that tanks in a mixed defence typically inflict casualties at a rate no higher than that commonly achieved in a battle between tanks alone. However the consistency of the results for mixed defences and for gun only defences does tend to bear out this assumption.

Index

Page references in *italics* denote figures and illustrations.

bombardment, relationship between density and duration on infantry
    firepower degradation 60–1, *61*
bomber 'streaming' 5–6
bombing, carpet 9
Bonaparte, Napoleon 1
Borneo (1963-66) 15, 98
Bredin, Brigadier 157–8
Britain, Battle of (1940) 188–9
British Army
    Airborne Division, 1st 154–5, *154*
    Anti-Aircraft (AA) Command 7
    anti-tank gun organisation in WW2 108
    Armoured Brigade, 1: 131
    Armoured Brigade, 4: 188
    Armoured Brigade, 22: 111, 188
    Armoured Division, 1st 133
    Armoured Division, 7th 112, 130
    Armoured Division, 79th 62
    Army, First 8, 111, 127
    Army, Eighth 8–9, 112, 188
    Army Operational Research Establishment (formerly AORG) 12
    Army Operational Research Group (AORG) 12
        established 7–8
        Field Studies Group (later DOAE Field Studies Division) 15
        Library Publication Section 11
        Photographic Liaison Section 11
        sections 10–11
    Army Operational Research Section (AORS) 1: 10
    Army Operational Research Section 2 (No 2 ORS) 8, 9, 10, 15–16
    Army Operational Research Sections 3-7: 10
    Army Operational Research Sections 8-10: 11
    Army Operational Research Unit Far East 14–15
    Army Personnel Research Establishment (APRE) 12
    Battle School 51
    Berlin Brigade 223–7
    Brigade, 4 (Guards) 55
    Director General of Army Training 46–7
    Division, 53rd (Welsh) 97
    Division, 78th 166
    Dragoon Guards, 4/7 *ii*, 107
    Grenadier Guards 84, *85*, 86
    Guards Brigade, 201: 112–13, *117*
    Gurkha battalions 155
    Gurkha regiments: defence effectiveness and gallantry awards 157–9,
        158, 159

Canadian Corps 50
Caplan, Lionel 158, 159
Capuzzo, battles of (1941) 137
Cassino Town, battles for (1944) 93
casualties
    attack
        attacks on defence positions needed to halve 97–8, *98*
        comparison of effects of attack AFV support 69–70, *69*
        per defence equivalent machine gun 96–7, *96*
        effect of force ratio on 83, *84*
        normal cumulative distribution 96, *96*
    defence, comparison between live and simulated 82–3, *83*
    effect of density of preparatory attack bombardment on 58–9, *59*
    effect of surprise on, per defensive machine gun 171, *171*
    infantry officer 9
    and mean local odds, relationship between 32, *34*
    Rifle Brigade, and awards (WW2) *152*, 153
    urban battle, comparison of 75, *78*
    urban battles, expected 90, *91*
    urban combat, standard ratios per defensive weapon 92–3, *93*
casualty estimates, machine gun, comparison of *57*, 58
casualty estimates, rifle, comparison of 55–6, *55*
casualty reduction factors 45, *46*
cavalry, horsed, role of 180
cavalry attack, shock effects of 180, 187, 198–9, 203, *204*
Centre for Defence Analysis, High-Level Studies Department
        (formerly Defence Operational Analysis Establishment) 12
Chaumont, France 91
chi-squared test 155, 209
Citta di Castello 189
Clausewitz, Karl von 1–2
close combat, approach to historical analysis of 215–16
Colenso, battle of (1899) 179, 200
Cologne raid (1942) 5–6
combat, close, in woods and forests 95–6, *96*
    effects of experience in 97, *98*
combat in areas of high relief 99–105, *102*, *104*
    advance rate and defence effectiveness, relationship between 101
    defence effectiveness, data for different nationalities 104, *104*
    effectiveness multipliers comparison 102–3, *102*, 104
    elevation of defence and increase in defence effectiveness, relationship
        between 99–100
    gradient 104, *104*

firepower degradation, infantry see infantry firepower degradation
First World War see World War 1
Forder, Dr R A 13, 14
forests, close combat in 95–6, *96*
    effects of experience in 97, *98*
Fort Halstead, RARDE 47
fortification 67
Francis, Corporal 116
Franco-Prussian War (1870) 55
Franklin, Benjamin 3
Frederick the Great 1
French cavalry 199, *204*
French defences in WW2 103
Fuller, Major General J F C 182–3

Gallabat, Sudan (1940) 189
gallantry 148–9 *see also* 'heroes', 'heroic action' and 'heroism' *entries*
gallantry awards
    artillery, at Arnhem 154–5, *155*
    British and Gurkha, comparison for 158–9, *158*, *159*
    British and Israeli measures, correlation of 156, *157*
    comparison of KIA ratios by rank and arm 150, *151*
    guns in anti-tank role, analysis for *152*, 153
    Gurkha defence effectiveness and, comparison of 157–9, *158*, *159*
    infantry, per fatal casualty 153–4, *153*
    Israeli and British measures, correlation of 156, *157*
    Israeli forces in Yom Kippur War 155, *156*
    Rifle Brigade in WW2 *152*, 153
Gazala, battle of (1942) 205
Gee navigation aid 6
Geilenkirchen salient 59
German Army
    Army, Fourth Panzer 194
    Army, Sixth 194–5
    Jaeger Regiment, 741: 189
    Light Division, 90th 187
    Panzer Army, Fifth 127
    Panzer Division, 10th 113
    Panzer Division, 15th 112, 188
    Panzer Division, 21st 113
German defensive actions in WW2 103
German infiltration tactics 185
German parachute infantry defence 93–4
German use of anti-tank guns in offensive roles 137

colonial troops 189
defensive actions in World Wars 103, 109
infantry brigade 187
Italy 8–9, 109, 206
German defensive actions in WW2 93, 103

Kagan, Jerome 165, *166*
Kephalonia, Italian defensive actions in WW2 103
King, Reverend Cecil 188–9
Kirby, M W 4
Korean War (1950-53) 14, 52, 103, 186–7
Kuneitra, Syria (1941) 91
Kwajalein atoll 60, *60*

Lanchester, F W 3
N-Squared Law of Combat 3, 35–6
Landrecies, defence of (1914) 55
Law of Combat, Lanchester N-Squared 3, 35–6
Leach, Dr J 165, *166*
Leadership 49, 126, 127 *see also* supervision
Leathart, Squadron Leader James 188
Libya 57, 137
local force ratio (odds), mean 32, *34*, *35*, 36
Lucas-Phillips, C E 123–4

machine gun, defence equivalent, attack casualties per 96–7, *96*
machine gun casualty estimates, comparison of *57*, 58
machine gun defence effectiveness and attack tank density
with anti-tank weapons 66–7, *67*
D-Day beaches 64, *64,* 68
summary of effects 69–73, *69*, 71
WW1 battles 66, *66*
WW2 battles 63, *63*, *64*, 65, 66
with zero fortification 67–8, *68*
machine gun fire, defence, effectiveness of 56–8, 57 *see also* weapons:
machine guns
Macksey, Major Kenneth 15
Makin atoll 60, *60*
Malayan Emergency (1948-60) 14–15, 98, 159
Maltot, France 91
Manston Mutiny 188–9
Mareth line 133
Marshall, Lt Col (later Brig Gen) S L A 51–2, 53, 56, 58, 70–1, 143,
165–6, *166*

THE STRESS OF BATTLE

anti-tank guns in WW2 107, 108, 109–11, 112, 113
   in a mobile role 131–3
defensive actions in WW2 103, 109, 110–11
and German anti-tank guns in offensive roles 137, 138
Western Desert WW2 tank/anti-tank battles 120, 121–2, *121*, 126,
   127–8

obstacles 67, 92
On War 1–2
Operation Clipper 59, 60, 62, 66
Operation Crusader 57, 131–2
Operation Overlord 59
Operation Veritable 59–60, *60*, 62, 63, *63*, 66
Operational Analysis (OA)/Operational Research (OR)
   Air Ministry takes lead in establishing 3–4
   first use of term OR 4
   function of 16
   in World War 2: 4–11, 13, 15–16, 32
   origins 1–5
   post-war changes 12–15
   RAF, official history of 1
   and use of field trials 214–15
Operational Requirements (OR) directorates 12
Operational Research (OR) *see* Operational Analysis
Operational Research Study, Second World War 62, 64
Ortona, assault on (1943) 93
Osipov, M 3
overkill 38–9, *39*, 42, *43*, 45, 48
overrun odds 36

Pacific atolls, US landings on 60, *60*
panic and shock 189–91, *192*, 194–5, *194*
Parry Roi atoll 60, *60*
Patton Jr, General George S 142, 221
Pepper, Lt, MC 132
personnel combat behaviour, insights into 220–1
Pitt, Barrie 187–8
Poland 201–2
portee, *see* anti-tank guns in mobile role
Priestley, Joseph 3
Proasteion Ridge (1941) 131